TEN BRAVE MEN

TEN BRAVE MEN

Makers of the American Way

WILLIAM BRADFORD ☆ ROGER WILLIAMS
☆ PATRICK HENRY ☆ SAMUEL ADAMS ☆
THOMAS JEFFERSON ☆ GEORGE WASHINGTON
☆ BENJAMIN FRANKLIN ☆ JOHN PAUL JONES ☆
ANDREW JACKSON ☆ ABRAHAM LINCOLN

By *Sonia Daugherty*

With Drawings by James Daugherty

J. B. LIPPINCOTT COMPANY, PUBLISHERS
PHILADELPHIA AND NEW YORK

I dedicate this book
to
all those who have the courage
to enlist against tyranny over
the minds of men

FOREWORD

"As soon as history is properly told, there is no more need of romances."—Walt Whitman

The ten great men in these stories were not different from any other boys when they were studying reading, writing and arithmetic. But they had one thing in common: they became interested in an idea, and they didn't stop there and forget it. They listened to the still small voice that talks to us all of things sublime; they made decisions which sent them on their way to glorious achievements.

The most daring adventurers in fiction cannot hold a candle to the men whose bold undertakings shape history. The Pilgrim Fathers didn't exactly plan the United States of America when they started out to worship God in freedom. Nor did Roger Williams know that he was laying the foundation for a great democracy when he ran away from the rule of the Elders in the Boston Bay Colony on a stormy night. And Patrick Henry may not have dreamed of a revolution when he dared to make his challenging speech in the House of Burgesses. But all great causes are born of necessity. When a wrong becomes too much to endure, it is a sign that the time for progress has come.

Many things happened that might have blighted these brave beginnings. But these men, who had wedded themselves to their ideals, fought against the enemies of progress as they fought against the savages and beasts in the wilderness with charmed weapons, forged by love for mankind, and a great faith.

Sonia Daugherty

Westport, Conn.

CONTENTS

WILLIAM BRADFORD
—— 1620 ——

"It is not with us as it is with other men whom small things can discourage. . . ."

IT WAS A COLD NOVEMBER MORNING; ONLY A FEW pale stars were still visible in the gray sky. The lookout on the starboard bow, watching the horizon, rubbed his eyes, hoping he was seeing aright—but there was no mistaking the dark line in the distance. "Land, ahoy," he shouted in such a voice as to rouse the

1

Mayflower into a sudden hubbub. Sailors scurried up the narrow gangways, shouting the welcome news; passengers tumbled out of their cramped bunks and rushed on deck to study the faint line on the horizon, hardly discernible in the gray light of dawn.

"Is it true?" Men and women, half dressed, shivered in the cold wind, rubbing sleep out of eyes weary with watching for so many days and nights, weeks and months. Children churned about their mothers, singing it out—"Land! Land!"

The smudge of an outline seemed to come nearer as the morning unfolded. "Land" the word went back and forth like a song. The fearful storms and constant perils of the long crossing were forgotten for the time being.

Everyone went about his business at last, dressing for the day, eating breakfast, doing chores. But now that the excitement was over, women gathered in groups to speculate—"What will it be like?" they asked each other, uneasily.

Mistress Elizabeth Hopkins nursed her infant Oceanus, born at sea. There would be no one to welcome the ship, she was thinking. No kindly eye to smile, no friendly voice to call out a greeting, no house to receive them, no inn, no store to replenish their needs. Her arms gripped the infant to her bosom with a sudden terror. Oceanus let out a lusty yell.

"Look to your babe," counseled Mistress Mary Brewster. She took the child into her motherly arms.

"It's a wilderness we're coming to," cried Mrs. Hopkins. "The savages are fierce and terrible. They may tear us limb from limb."

"Ay," broke in Mrs. Billington sharply. "These savages cut off the scalps—and let you bleed to death. And that's not all. It's a fierce wilderness, wild beasts and snakes. We'll starve to death maybe."

Mrs. Brewster trundled the infant in silence awhile, searching in her mind for words that might comfort the younger women who had now gathered in a cluster around her.

"We had fears such as these when we first thought to undertake the journey. Terrible tales were told us of the loneliness in the wilderness and the fierce ways of savages. Some were against the venture"—Mrs. Brewster rocked the child in her arms in silence awhile—"We might have remained in comfort at Leyden to the end of our days if we had given in to our fears—we might have grown old and died there—exiles in a foreign land."

"I wish we had, I wish we had," cried young Mistress Dorothy Bradford.

"It was for an honorable cause we came here," reminded Mrs. Brewster gently.

"Honorable?" questioned Mrs. Billington with a dubious smile.

"Ay, to build us a new world, our own world where we might worship God in freedom. When we were all decided on that, we knew also that God would care for us at sea and in the wilderness."

"Leyden is beautiful," brooded Mistress Bradford. "We had comforts, and pretty things. My husband owned a factory and it prospered well. All this we gave up to come here, and maybe die by the hand of savages or starve to death." She turned and walked away to think her thoughts in silence.

Mistress Brewster looked from Dorothy to the group of men talking with the captain of the ship. Her glance rested with affection on the thoughtful young face of William Bradford. "Dorothy is young," she said quietly. "When she grows older, she will understand that William is not an ordinary man. We knew him back in Scrooby, England, when he was but a lad. He gave up more than Dorothy knows about; for he might have inherited the goodly lands of his uncles, had he not chosen to join himself with the society separate from the established English church."

"The Separatists!" cried Mrs. Billington. "What good was that?"

"To keep close to the written word of God, so as to receive from God Himself the meaning, with no bishops and no ceremonies," explained Mrs. Brewster in her kind motherly voice.

"His friends and his relations should have kept that young man from such foolishness," said Mistress Hopkins.

"His friends tried to prevent him from it, they mocked and derided," said Mistress Brewster with a reminiscent smile. "His uncles warned him, he would be disinherited if he persisted in attending the separatist church. To all of them young William gave but one answer—'I am not only willing to part with everything that is dear to me in this world for this cause, but I am also thankful that God has given me a heart so to do,' he told them." Mistress Brewster remained silent awhile, remembering it all. "For this cause we left our homes in England, and lived in exile in Holland, and it is for this cause we came here. God brought us here for a good purpose," she added, looking down at Oceanus fast asleep in her arms.

Mrs. Billington sniffed. She and her husband had small patience with these Pilgrims, always praying and singing psalms. And yet, she could not deny that when the winds blew out of the west for days on end, until the sails were blown down, and the helmsman was unable to hold the ship in the face of roaring gales, and the ship floundered through monstrous seas, and lay on her bow end, and the lashings forced water through opened-up seams on deck, the Pilgrims knelt and prayed, and sang psalms though the end seemed nigh. At the time it happened, it did seem as if the hand of God had righted the ship and brought them safe across. But Mrs. Billington had no mind for idle speculations; her two mischievous boys were enough to look after. She went off now to search for them.

Mrs. Hopkins took Oceanus from Mrs. Brewster. All this might be as Mrs. Brewster said, she was thinking. Mr. Hopkins had been a deacon at one time, and a quoter of scriptures, though he was now in search of adventure to mend their fortunes. She glanced towards the men, talking in low voices. They were all adventurers on this boat, she thought to herself, each one looking for something.

Captain Jones was trying to explain this to the Pilgrims. Ever since it had become known that the *Mayflower* was to land in New England and not in Virginia as it had been given out at the beginning of the journey, there had been rumors of a plot hatching among the "Strangers." "We shall use our own liberty when we land," they had been heard to say. The "Strangers" were not of the Pilgrim company. Why they were coming to this wilderness no one knew. Perhaps they didn't know themselves as yet. But here they were. The Pilgrims had befriended them all through the journey with many kindnesses. The captain's sympathy was with the Pilgrims, not only because they were kind and gentle with each other, but they had been considerate to the crew and to everyone aboard ship. "It is a bad business," he said, scratching his beard. "No one in New England has authority over them, after they leave my ship."

"We need every able-bodied man to help build before the winter weather sets in," reasoned John Carver. A merchant and a man of substance, as well as a searcher for freedom, he spoke with authority.

"The patent is for Virginia." In Virginia they would be obliged to hold to the agreement of the patent, reminded the captain, knowing full well that the Pilgrims would refuse to go to Virginia where they would be obliged to worship according to the Anglican bishops they had run away from in England.

"This we have no mind to do," protested Elder Brewster.

The answer suited Captain Jones; it was not by accident he had come to New England, but by secret agreement with the company.

"We might find a likely place along the Hudson," suggested young William Bradford. "We have heard a good report in Holland about the settlement on the Hudson."

Captain Jones pursed his lips. Dutch settlers on the Hudson were not over anxious for English settlers. He had received a generous present from them, and made a tentative promise.

All that morning the *Mayflower* followed a course southward, close to the shore, and came suddenly into dangerous shoals and roaring breakers; night was coming on. Facing danger, the ship headed back into the open sea.

No one slept much that night. The Pilgrims had ample time to meditate and to pray. They had been nearly four months on this journey, what with delays due to leaking ships, mendings and changings from ship to ship. They were ninety-eight days out of Southampton, sixty-six days out of Plymouth, and now it was November. Nor did the Strangers sleep much that night, laying their plans in whispers.

It was still early morning when the *Mayflower* rounded the tip of the cape and found a harbor on a stretch of white sand—Cape

Cod, the captain knew it was, named about ten years before by Captain John Smith who had found it full of fish.

The anchor went down with a great rattling and noise. The ship trembled and rocked for a moment and suddenly stood still. A great shout went out—"We're anchored"—The children and the younger women gathered at the rail, impatient to go ashore— "Earth, sand," cried Priscilla, the vivacious young daughter of Mullen the London shopkeeper. She tried to get off the ship to walk about, and stretch her legs.

"No one is to go ashore until Captain Jones gives the order," a stern-faced young mate informed her grimly.

"Where's the captain?" demanded young Edward Dotey insolently. The mate studied the fellow's face with a disdainful glance. Dotey was only one of Master Hopkins' servants, and so was Edward Leister, also demanding to be allowed on shore.

The captain was nowhere to be seen, for he was in consultation with the Pilgrims in his cabin.

"It would be most cruel to let the children and the women go ashore without assurance that shelter would be built before winter sets in," Elder Brewster was saying.

"If we offered to make a pact with the Strangers, something after the covenant of our church in Leyden, it may be that they would change their minds and unite with us," proposed William Bradford.

"Ay," agreed John Carver thoughtfully. "If you would write it out," he said to Elder Brewster, "Captain Jones might read it aloud for all to hear."

"That will not take me long to do," said Elder Brewster as he hurried away to find a copy of the covenant among his papers.

"If we but win Captain Miles Standish to us, the others would follow, I think," exclaimed William Bradford hopefully.

"Ay, he is much admired, it seems," said Captain Jones. "But we cannot delay this thing too long," he added.

Bradford hurried off to help Elder Brewster compose the pact.

The women and the children assembled on deck to watch the water, and to peer fearfully into the distance beyond the shore, where a dark woods shut out the horizon. What was there, in that woods? they asked each other, imagining frightful beasts and savages. A gentle breeze ruffled the water. Fish came to the surface to disport themselves in the pale November sunshine. "Whales," shouted several excited voices suddenly. Everyone crowded to the rail to stare at the whales lying there, inert and immense.

"Oil and bone, men, there's a fortune in these monsters," whispered Billington. The whale nearest the ship lay so still, it might be dead, thought young Dotey. He ran for a musket and fired a shot to see if the creature would stir. The musket exploded and flew to pieces. No one was hurt, but the whale, awakened from his dreams, flipped and swam away. The other whales followed.

"A fortune in oil and bones," ruminated Billington half aloud. "Let's get off this boat, get our things, get off, get started . . ."

"No one is to go ashore until Captain Jones gives the order," reminded the mate, noticing the hasty preparations to leave the ship. "Captain Jones wants every man to come on deck; he has something he wants to say."

"Well then," snapped Billington. "Let's go up there and get it over with."

Miles Standish was already there, when the rest of the Strangers straggled up on deck.

Captain Jones eyed his passengers in silence for a moment, the quiet expectant faces of the "saints," and the impatient sullen faces of the Strangers. He held up a white sheet of paper and waved it in the air to attract attention—"It has become known that you have intentions to strike out alone without the Pilgrims. Is this true?" he asked, looking pointedly at each of the Strangers.

"It is our right to do as we choose to do," snapped the red-bearded little Captain Miles Standish. "There is no one here who has authority over us."

"That may be so," broke in William Bradford. "There is only your conscience to dictate to you here."

"We've not crossed this wide ocean to come here to talk about conscience," cried Captain Standish impatiently.

"Ay," sniffed Billington. "We've not come to saddle ourselves with a conscience, and maybe starve to death. We've come here to find ways to make our fortune before others come and make themselves masters."

"We have come here not to make a fortune, nor to make ourselves masters, but to build a new world, a free world for others as well as for ourselves. God has brought us safe across the vast and furious ocean to fulfill this purpose," said Bradford, looking away from Billington to Miles Standish.

"We're no praying Pilgrims; we're looking for ways to mend our fortunes," said the doughty little captain with a sneer. He had been to wars, and he had been in brawls and in feuds. He was not given to arguing. "We do not intend to perish for no profitable end."

"Have you forgotten how often we have been saved when we were at the pit's brim and in danger?" reminded Bradford. "God will not let us perish. He has a purpose for bringing us here. We therefore ask you to join us in a pact."

"What kind of a pact?" demanded the red-bearded captain, touched into curiosity by Bradford's manner.

Captain Jones cleared his throat; the paper rustled in the wind. He began to read in a loud clear voice ". . . In the name of God. Amen. We whose names are underwritten . . . do by these present, solemnly and mutually in the presence of God, and one another, covenant and combine ourselves together into a civil body politic . . . and by virtue hereof, to enact, constitute and frame such just and equal laws . . . as shall be thought most mete and convenient for the general good of the colonie, unto which we promise all due submission and obedience . . ." He looked up from the paper to glance swiftly from face to face.

A sailor had brought a pot of ink and a quill. Captain Jones laid the pact on an upturned barrel.

John Carver dipped the quill into the ink and wrote his name with a loud scratching on the stiff paper.

"God has brought us over a vast and furious ocean, and delivered us from the perils so that we may do His will, and fulfill His purpose," said Elder Brewster, writing his name and giving the quill to Bradford, standing at his side.

Bradford glanced challengingly at Miles Standish and wrote his name in silence.

Billington and his cronies were also watching Miles Standish as he stood there, frowning. He came of a great house; noble passions were not unfamiliar to him. He studied the pact, considering it word by word, and suddenly he leaned over, and put his name down in a bold flourish.

A long uneasy silence among the Strangers followed. They had counted on Miles Standish to take part in their plans. They whispered among themselves now, and came over to sign at last.

Edward Dotey and Edward Leister were amazed as were the other servants when they were invited to put their names down equally with their masters.

"We are now a united body politic, let us therefore proceed to vote for a governor," proposed Elder Brewster.

"What need we of governor if we are all equal?" demanded Billington gruffly.

"To serve us, and to look after our affairs," explained Brewster.

Everyone looked instinctively to John Carver. He had been wise, and he had been considerate of everyone in the trying days aboard ship. They crowded around to cast their vote into a sailor's hat.

The captain sorted the votes with a smile of satisfaction—"You have elected John Carver without an opposite," he announced.

Twenty men, interrupted by a sudden snowstorm and crowded into a flimsy shelter, were impatient to go back to work. But they were used to snowstorms, rain and wind by now. It was not the snow that worried them, but the delay—

"It is nigh to two months since we touched harbor at Cape Cod, and we haven't a house to shelter us yet," exclaimed Hopkins.

William Bradford took his saw and walked to the clearing before the woods. It had taken many weeks of weary searching in foul weather and fair, to find this place. Standing on a stump of a tree, he could see the harbor, and the hill rising above it a short distance away. There was a river at the foot of the hill, and cleared fields beside the river. Savages must have cleared these fields and grown corn there; but so far, there was not a sign of them. New Plymouth was a good name for this pleasant harbor, he mused.

"Divine Providence has guided us to this place," he said half aloud and half to himself. "It is well we built the platform on the hill before the snows set in," he said to Winslow who had walked up to stand beside him.

"We can be thankful we have that mount from whence to watch both sea and land." Winslow walked up and down in silence a while, thinking of something he had on his mind. "The savages are encamped not far away," he came back to say. "On clear days I have seen smoke from their fires."

"I have been thinking that we do wrong to fear the savages," said Bradford. "They run away from us when they see us, which is a sign they fear us also, even though they attacked us that time whilst we were still at Cape Cod. When we fired our muskets, they cried out in fear and ran away. Therefore if we show them that we wish to be their friends, we can win them to us."

"How can this be accomplished when we do not know how to speak to them?" young Winslow asked.

"Always, when we needed guidance, we prayed to our Father, and He gave us directions," reminded Bradford.

The wind had shifted southward suddenly, the sky cleared and it stopped snowing. The men went back to work in the woods. The frosty stillness rang presently with the blows of axes and screechings of saws. Felled trees toppled over with strange moaning sounds, as if in protest, or perhaps it was only the wind in the bare branches.

Francis Billington and young Dotey dawdled over a tree they were pretending to drag. "I've not crossed that vast ocean to be felling trees and building houses for these praying Pilgrims," grumbled Billington.

"Nor I," growled Dotey. "I thought I'd go free and be my own master."

"I'll not remain here," said Billington. "Hard work never made anyone rich."

"Where'll you go?" asked Dotey eagerly.

"There's good hunting on Cape Cod. You can come along if you want to; there are a few others might come— We might take off in the shallop on a dark night," planned Billington.

Dotey listened entranced. He had come here as one of Master Hopkins' bondsmen. It would be five years before he would be free. "Whales come close to shore on Cape Cod," he said in an excited whisper. "If we could get harpoons now." In his excitement he stopped work and stood there, his hands on his hips, listening to Billington's plan.

"This is no time for idling," reproved William Bradford, striding up suddenly. He had been observing the two for some time, and noticed how they idled while others worked. "The *Mayflower* may sail back to England any time now and we have no shelter to move to as yet," he reminded them.

"I'm not here to take orders from anyone," cried Billington in sudden anger, brandishing his axe.

"Your name is written on the pact to abide by the common good." Bradford turned to Dotey, ignoring Billington's threatening gesture.

Dotey looked from Billington's cunning angry face to Bradford. There was something in the calm kindness of Bradford's look and voice that made him feel suddenly ashamed of plotting with Billington. He moved instinctively towards the older man.

"Help me drag that log to the hill," said Bradford, indicating a fallen tree a few paces away.

Again Dotey looked at Billington, still brandishing his axe; there was murder in Billington's face.

"I'll not be going away from here," he said in a frightened voice. "I'll stay and abide by the covenant."

Billington threw his axe after Bradford and Dotey. Miles Standish had knit himself with those Pilgrims, getting thicker and thicker with them, and now, this fool Dotey, was following after that Bible-reading Bradford. Let those fools toil and sweat, and die of starvation in this wilderness, he fumed. As for himself, he would find a man or two to go off with him, find a place of their own, and find ways to get at those whales.

At the *Mayflower* that evening, Governor Carver was holding council with Elder Brewster and Miles Standish.

"Now that the platform on the mount is built, the Common House must be completed speedily," he was saying. "We'll move our goods from the ship to keep in the Common House, and give out equally to each one as the need is."

"Keep everything in common. It will be a simple way to manage," agreed Brewster.

"Savages have been seen hereabouts," broke in Miles Standish. "The cannon must be transferred from the *Mayflower* to the platform on the hill."

"A far better way to protect ourselves is to find ways to make friends with the savages," said William Bradford, who had just come in from work in the woods.

"Ay," nodded Carver, "if we make friends with the savages, we shall not need the cannon."

"Until then, we must be prepared to defend ourselves," insisted Miles Standish.

Bradford drew a line from the beach to the hill. "We'll build our houses close together, a small garden for each house. It will be our street."

Bradford spoke in sadness as he planned the new homes. He was not planning a house for himself. His wife Dorothy had been drowned while he was away on an expedition. The women came nearer to sit and listen to the plans, forgetting the hardships and the fears in planning gardens for tomorrow.

But all plans were interrupted presently. A terrible sickness broke out on the *Mayflower* like a scourge. Men who had waded in icy water from the ship to the shallop to get ashore while at Cape Cod, were now lying sick with fever, and hacking coughs. Scurvy had set in. Women caring for the sick were taking the sickness. Those who were still about watched over the children with tender devotion. The children must live to inherit the promised land. But men and women were dying, three a day sometimes. The burials took place at night, and graves were covered with leaves so Indians wouldn't know.

Captain Miles Standish forgot he was a soldier and looked after the sick with the tender devotion of a woman. Bradford, limping on inflamed ankles, washed the "loathsome" clothes of the sick, dressed and undressed them, fed them, and administered what remedies there were, and fell a prey to the sickness, and Governor Carver also. They recovered; but Miles Standish was not able to save Rose, his wife, in spite of all his care of her.

There was no time to weep for the dead, no time for mourning. Every man, able to move about, went out to work. The Common House was presently completed. For the time being, it was a hospital where the sick lay on cots.

There was no need for as many houses as had been planned, for only fifty-one out of the hundred and two were left; only five out of the eighteen wives remained. But the children were spared. Their blithe young voices broke the quietness of the somber days.

Captain Jones was not talking about sailing back to England these days. He had lost many of his crew and officers, and those who were left were still recovering their strength after the illness.

Indians hiding in the woods throughout the winter were beginning to make their presence known as the month of March advanced and brought long golden days of sunshine. A company of them appeared on the other side of the brook one day. They displayed their bows and arrows and made threatening gestures.

Miles Standish waded across the brook to talk to them, hoping that somehow they might come to an understanding; but the savages ran away, yelling out threats. They would come back. The cannon was laboriously dragged to the platform on the hill, for the women and children had been moved from the *Mayflower* to the cottages.

Spring had come at last; birds sang, wild flowers scented the crisp warm air. The children came out to frolic in the street, while the women worked in their tiny gardens. Today they were planting seeds to grow cabbages, but already they were whispering about the flowers that would bloom in their gardens before very long.

Suddenly, a tall powerful looking Indian, carrying a bow and arrow, crossed the clearing and came striding up the street. The women gathered the children, dashed into their houses, and barricaded the doors. The men had just sat down to a meeting in the Common House when they saw the savage at the door.

"Welcome, English," called out the Indian.

They stood staring at him, not knowing what to expect. He was naked from head to foot, excepting for a narrow strip in his middle. "I want beer," he announced.

But there was no beer. The Pilgrims went to find what they might give him to make up for it: "Strong water" (brandy), biscuits and butter, cheese, a piece of a duck and pudding. It was fortunate Captain Jones had shot a mallard only the day before and brought it to them.

The Indian ate and talked. "Samoset my name," he told them. He had learned English, he explained, from fishermen who came to Maine in ships. The Pilgrims listened to his tales with astonishment. He was from Maine, he informed them. He told them about the different tribes. The tribe that had occupied the territory they were occupying now, had been wiped out by a plague three years ago. That explained to them the reason the ground had been cleared and no Indians had come to drive them away.

The afternoon was drawing to a close, a chill wind cooled the air. The Pilgrims threw a horseman's red cloak over Samoset to keep him warm. He liked the cloak and the food and his friendly hosts. It was time for him to go away, but he made it plain he had no intention of leaving. There was nothing to do but lodge him for the night. Stephen Hopkins consented to put him up with a guard to watch him, lest he massacre them all in their sleep. But Samoset had no such intention. He consented to go away the next day after receiving presents of a knife, a bracelet and a ring. "I will come bring Indians to trade," he promised as he took his leave at last, holding his gifts proudly.

The street churned with excited expectation for several days, but no Samoset appeared. Then one day, just as the Pilgrims were about to sit down to complete the business of the interrupted meeting, Samoset appeared with another Indian. "He Squanto, he speak better English," Samoset introduced his friend.

Squanto was in the middle of relating how he had been kidnapped by Spanish traders and sold for a slave in England when Samoset interrupted to inform the Pilgrims that the great chief Massasoit and his men were waiting on Strawberry Hill, the other side of the brook. Massasoit, Samoset explained in his queer English, would not come to the Pilgrims. They must go to meet him on the hill.

"This is a trap to massacre us," whispered several of the more cautious. The Pilgrims went aside to reason it out among themselves.

"It may be a plot, and yet, Samoset has shown us that the savages can be friendly," reasoned Bradford.

"If that chief intended to be friendly, he would be willing to come to us," said Hopkins.

"We have been praying to find ways to make friends with the savages," broke in young Winslow. "Let me go to the chief with Samoset as my interpreter."

There was some uneasy arguing, but Winslow prevailed. He set out with gifts in his hands: a pot of "strong water," two knives, biscuits and a copper chain with a jewel on it.

Massasoit was delighted with the gifts. His solemn face, smeared with streaks of paint, broke out into a smile. He listened with deep interest to Winslow's speech, translated by Samoset. Governor Carver, Winslow said, hoped to make friends with the great chief Massasoit. The King of England, he said, hoped that he and Massasoit would be united in friendship forever and do much trading.

Massasoit liked the speech, and consented to visit Governor Carver at once.

Presently a strange procession came striding up the street. The savages, a head taller than the Pilgrims, their faces painted in stripes and crosses, looked fierce enough to frighten anyone. But they had left their bows and arrows on the other side of the river. The women and children lined up against the houses to watch the visitors in awed silence.

A green carpet had been hurriedly spread on the floor of the largest house to receive the chief. No sooner was Massasoit seated on a cushion than a blare of trumpets and beating of drums started up, and Governor Carver entered, accompanied by several men wearing corselets, and carrying muskets. Massasoit stood up, startled and uneasy, but greatly impressed. He kissed Governor Carver's hand, and the Governor kissed the chieftain's greasy hand in return. Governor Carver then offered him a drink of "strong water." Massasoit took a long draught. He was not used to such strong drink; a sweat broke out all over him. But he liked the drink and the food.

Governor Carver lost no time now in proposing a treaty. He had it written out, and read it aloud with Samoset translating. They were not to do any hurt to one another in any way. If an Indian broke the treaty, he was to be sent to the white men to be punished. If a white man broke the treaty, he was to be sent to the Indians to be punished. The chief made a mark for a signature, and Governor Carver signed his name.

It was April at last; wildflowers scented the woods, the sun made golden shadows on the budding trees, birds sang, and the black earth smelled sweet.

Captain Jones was sailing back to England. He came ashore to bid his passengers farewell. "Does anyone wish to go back?" he asked the company assembled at the Common House to honor him.

The women lighted candles, for it was now dusk. The gaunt faces, bronzed by wind and sun, and marked with weariness after a day of toil in the fields, looked back at him with a strange quietness, seeing him, and seeing England in their mind's eye, and seeing something else that only each one knew for himself.

"Go back?" William Bradford's voice rang out in astonishment. His eyes swept the assembly as if to question each one, and his glance rested for a moment on Miles Standish. He had not joined their church, but he came to pray with them, and Dotey also, and all the other young men; they were knit together now by a common bond that was stronger than the written pact.

"Will no one go back then?" marveled Captain Jones. "It is a hard life you have chosen, and yet, I almost wish to share it with you," he added, seeing something in these faces he had come to know so well, something different, something new shining there behind those eyes. "It is a hard life you have chosen," he repeated with a wistful note.

"It is not with us as it is with other men whom small things can discourage, or small discontentments cause to wish themselves at home again," said Bradford quietly.

Perhaps the captain understood all that this meant when he went back to the ship at last, his pockets bulging with letters to take back to England.

A brisk wind slapped the sea. The ship rocked gently as the waves lapped against her sides. The crew and officers were impatient to be off. Captain Jones turned in the shallop for a last word with his friends who had come to see him off. "It is not too late to change your minds and go back," he said, half in earnest half in jest. They smiled, but there were tears in their eyes, he noted. The cannon went off, a signal for the departure. Captain Jones climbed from the shallop to the ship, the anchor was lifted, the sails swelled out. The *Mayflower* rocked, and moved slowly.

The waves reached out to the shore with long fingers. No one stirred. The *Mayflower* was going away, she was going out to sea across the wide Atlantic. They were on their own now. They waved their hands, their kerchiefs fluttered in the breeze; they kept on waving, watching the ship plow through the sea. They were alone in their new world, to make it what they chose, out of their own courage and faith.

ROGER WILLIAMS

—— 1636 ——

"I must proclaim before the Most Holy God, angels, and men that . . . this persecution for cause of conscience is a foul, a black, and a bloody tenet."

A HIGH WIND WHISTLED IN THE CHIMNEY AND PLAStered the fast falling snow against the windows of the clapboard house. In the living room a comfortable fire burned on the hearth. It was a simple room, with few luxuries, except for a number of handsome books and pewter candlesticks. Roger Williams glanced at the windows, adjusted a log in the grate and settled back in his chair. He had been recently ill, and he had not quite recovered as yet. His handsome face, with a high forehead and deep set eyes, was pale and drawn.

Mary Williams glanced up at her husband anxiously. "You need a rest," she said. "I am mighty thankful that the Elders at the Bay have consented to let you remain in Salem until spring."

"It is not a rest I need, but peace of mind," said Roger.

Mary remained silent awhile, thinking of their plight. "Let's go back to England," she exclaimed suddenly.

"That I will not," cried Roger. There was a touch of indignation in his voice. "I crossed three thousand miles of salt water to be free of the rule of bishops, and though I find that here, in Massachusetts, the Elders of the church rule the clergy and dictate what a minister should preach, yet I have hopes that this can be changed."

"Changed?" exclaimed Mary. "How can anything be changed here so long as the Elders of the church are also judges and magistrates of the state?"

Roger stood up and began to walk up and down the room restlessly. "Ay, in England there is an alliance between church and state, and we complained of that. And here it is worse—the state is ruled by the church. The Elders have power to force a man to go to church and pay tithes, whether he wishes or not. No, my dear, I shall not go back to England. I shall remain here and preach that every man has a right to a free conscience. Every man has a right to decide for himself how to worship his God. Every man has a right to decide for himself whether he should go to church or not as his own conscience directs."

"I almost wish that you had not quarreled with the Elders," sighed Mary. "They were kind to you when we first came from England. They offered you a place to teach in their church."

"So they did, my dear. But how could I accept the position when I discovered that the church of Massachusetts had not separated from the church of England, as I expected, and that I was to preach under the supervision of the Elders, and not what God directed me to preach. I had no choice but to decline."

A loud knock startled them both into silence. Roger hurried to the door and opened it cautiously. And recognizing the five muffled figures stamping snow from their heavy boots, he ushered them into the room with exclamations of warm welcome.

"Not even the storm can keep us away," exclaimed the younger of the two women.

"I am thankful to you for coming," said Roger cordially. Mary bustled about helping the callers dispose of their wraps and scarfs, while Roger arranged chairs and benches around the fire to seat them all.

The soft candle light threw wavering shadows on the faces of hosts and visitors, uncommon faces, still young, but already stamped with a will to endure all things for the sake of what they believed was right.

"What think you, William Harris, have the Elders a right to banish him?" asked the young woman of one of the men.

"The trial lasted a whole year. It was hard for them to prove that they were right," said William Harris in a contemptuous voice.

"It took that long because they're in the wrong, and they tried to prove they are right. Now that they've decreed to banish you, we're no longer to hear you preach," cried the older woman sadly. "And there are so many of us who dearly wish to hear you."

"That's what troubles the Elders; they're afraid Roger Williams' preaching will teach people to think for themselves, and that would deprive them of their authority," cried a young miller who had come all the way from Dorchester to hear Roger preach.

"We knew we had hardships ahead of us when we left England: cold, hunger, hard work," ruminated William Harris, who had come on the same ship with Roger. "But we didn't know we'd have the Elders at the Bay to badger us, and tell us what to think, and how to worship."

"Ay, we had great hopes, a free country, a new life, Roger Williams talked about teaching the savages the word of God," broke in the older man, who had been silent until now.

"I have not changed my mind," reminded Roger Williams.

"There are those who think as I do. They know there should be reforms, but they find it more convenient to agree with the Elders. I do not find fault with them, though I cannot do likewise."

"The Elders were all for banishing Roger at once, but Governor Winthrop prevailed on them to let us remain here in Salem till spring, provided Roger does not preach the while," said Mary. "I am mighty thankful to remain while Roger is still ill, and the children are so small."

"They have me silenced for the time being," smiled Roger. "But it is pleasant to know I have a friend in Governor Winthrop, and Winslow has been a friend to me at Plymouth on many occasions—"

Mary went to the kitchen and came back presently with a tray of warm drinks. They sat by the fire and talked, making plans.

"Where will you go when spring comes?" asked William Harris.

"I have not thought as yet." Roger tried to dismiss the subject.

The guests looked around at the comfortable room. "Your trading post is thriving. The Indians trust you. It is a pity you will have to abandon it," sympathized the older man.

"Ay, we are at last in comfortable circumstances," admitted Roger Williams. "Now we have to abandon our home, and my business." His pale face took on an angry look. "I am more troubled that a handful of men have acquired power to rule by a hard law." He pounded his hand on the arm of his chair—"The business of the church is with the souls of men, not with their goods and bodies; the business of the state is to look after the civil rights, and let the preachers speak as God directs."

The door latch rattled suddenly. Mary went to the door and opened it a crack. A man wrapped in a heavy cloak pushed his way into the room. He looked around at the company gathered before the fire and frowned:

"You are forbidden to preach at your house, Roger Williams! You know that well enough, and yet it has been reported to the Elders at the Bay that you continue to preach. I wish I could deny it, but I have caught you at it tonight."

"Surely we have a right to hold conversation with our friends," said Mary with a placating smile.

"The Elders don't go into whether its friends or foe listen. When Roger Williams speaks, it is always about freedom of conscience. Isn't that what he's been talking about?" the man asked ironically.

The company around the fire remained silent, their veiled eyes hiding their thoughts.

"I've come out in the storm to warn you that Captain Underhill and fourteen men are on their way even now to arrest you and put you aboard ship now riding at Nantucket, bound for England."

"By what right?" cried out several voices in protest.

"The Elders rule in Salem as well as at the Bay, and Plymouth is with them," reminded the man. He spoke in a firm voice, but it was plain he was not in sympathy with the Elders, and was only accepting their rule because it was easier to get along that way.

The group around the fire rose to go, now talking in low voices.

"Look to yourself," said the man, lifting his hand in a warning gesture. "Once you are committed to the ship, you'll be bound for England. And once you are in England you will find it hard to return. The Elders would see to that."

"Ay," agreed several gloomy voices. "The Elders would never let you step out of a ship on any of their territory." There was anger in their faces, but they dared not say more and crowded around Roger to whisper cautious words of advice.

Roger pressed their hands in a silent farewell as they went out at last into the night. Only the stranger remained now.

"Captain Underhill may be here any minute," he snapped in a low quick voice, and went out after the others.

Mary dropped down into a chair, her face in her hands. Roger stood before the fire, deep in thought. "I have no time to lose," he exclaimed after a minute. "I must be gone before Captain Underhill comes." He began to rummage among his papers on the desk.

"Why not go back to England?" cried Mary, rising from her chair with an air of determination. "What have we here in this wilderness but trouble and hardships?"

Roger did not seem to hear her. He had found the letter he was looking for. He sat down before the fire and read it over slowly.

"We have friends in England," Mary was saying. "Learned men

in high position think well of your talents and of your ability to preach. Mistaken though some of them may be, about their doctrine, it is a civilized country; and a better way of living. You would certainly be appointed to a church where your talents would be appreciated. You would be promoted, and perhaps end up a bishop."

Roger Williams heard not a word of what Mary said. He read the letter over several times as if understanding a hidden meaning in it now. ". . . Go out into the wilderness . . . find a place out of the jurisdiction of the Bay Colony . . ." He folded the letter and remained staring into the fire. Governor Winthrop must have known when he wrote him this letter that the Elders had been thinking of banishing him to England, he mused.

"I have no time to lose, my dear," he exclaimed again and began to arrange the papers on his desk into a file. "Captain Underhill must not find me when he gets here."

"If you'd promise not to speak so freely," brooded Mary. "The Elders might let you remain and let you preach. You might even win their good will and gain a reputation here."

"Shall I change for the sake of a little puff of credit and reputation and gain praise from the changeable breath of uncertain sons of men?" asked Roger sternly.

"I know you will not," she said tenderly. "Nor would I wish it."

He went to stand beside the crib of his newborn daughter fast asleep under the snug covers. He had named her Freeborn, in defiance of his judges. Freeborn, the name took on a sweeter and a grander meaning as he stood there.

"What have you decided to do?" whispered Mary coming to stand at his side.

"There is only one thing I can do. I must go at once and find Massasoit's winter lodge, and seek shelter until spring comes."

"How would you find Massasoit's camp in the dead of winter? You are still too ill to wander around in a blizzard like this. It is probably fifty miles deep in the woods. You wouldn't know which way to turn to find it." Mary began to weep helplessly.

"I know the general direction. I would steer my way by compass, South to West. Come what may, I will remain and fight it out with

God's help. Tell me you understand, tell me you are with me on this," he begged.

Mary stopped crying and dried her tears hastily.

"What am I doing, wasting time weeping?" She began to bustle about, packing a knapsack with provisions.

Roger tiptoed up the steep narrow stairs to the cold bedroom above, where his daughter Mary, two years old, was fast asleep. He leaned over and kissed her tenderly on the cheek.

"It is well we still have the trading post," he said, standing at his desk again, jotting down instructions for her on a sheet of paper. "The Indians know you, and they trust you; continue to trade with them. It will keep you and the children provided for. Tom is a good servant, he will look after you, and provide wood, and do the chores. We have friends. They will comfort you, and provide you with cheer." He sat down beside her for a few last words. "I will send you a message as soon as it is feasible. Spring is not far away. I will find a safe harbor, and build us a new home."

"If only I could know you will not perish on the way!"

"We have always trusted God to care for us," he reminded her.

"Yes, I know it. He will care for you," she brushed her tears away again and began to roll a blanket together. He put on his cloak and she wound a scarf around him. He was bundled to his ears now, his knapsack and his blanket were strapped to his back. She handed him his musket. They stood together for a moment.

"We are in the hands of Providence," his voice rang out, clear and confident.

She remained standing in the doorway, praying for him as he trudged away into the thick cloud of snow.

A party of Indian hunters came out of the woods. The tracks of heavy boots attracted their attention. Game was scarce. They didn't want a white man hunting in their vicinity. They scattered to watch.

But Roger Williams was not thinking of hunting as he plodded laboriously through the snow. He was alone in the great immensity of sky, gigantic fir trees, and an endless blanket of white snow. He had lost count of time. Was it two days or three since he left his home? It had stopped snowing at last. He looked at his compass; he was heading towards the woods he could now see in the near distance. Would Massasoit receive him in a friendly way?

He felt hungry most of the time. The food in his knapsack satisfied his hunger for a while, but it did not warm him. Only when he walked, making as much headway as was possible in the crusty snow, was he able to keep warm. It was at night, when he slept for a while in whatever shelter he could find, that he felt the cold biting into his very bones. There was no way to find out how far he had walked, excepting that he felt very tired. Night had come on again, beautiful with stars shining on the white snow, but he dreaded these cold nights with wolves baying in the distance. He crept into a clump of shrubs, laid the musket beside him, wrapped himself into his cloak and blanket, and fell into a deep sleep.

He must have slept a long while. When he wakened, it was broad daylight. He rubbed his eyes with the stiff knuckles of his hands. Was he dreaming, or was he actually seeing two dark, fiercely frowning faces, smeared with streaks of paint, and dank black hair hanging loose. He lifted his hand in a sign of peace, and clambered to his feet as fast as he could manage. The two red men pointed to his gun and made threatening gestures. And then suddenly a wide smile appeared on the face of the older Indian.

"You friend in Plymouth," he cried out. "You give medicine to squaw. You talk to Massasoit, you friend," he added gleefully.

"I am looking for Massasoit," explained Roger Williams eagerly. He had learned enough of the Indian language at Plymouth, and in trading with them at Salem to be able to help them on many occasions. And now he found himself able to answer the curious questions of both Indians, and to allay their fears about his gun.

Satisfied with his answers, the two red men were now willing to lead him to their Sachem Massasoit. It was still several hours walk. Noting how the white man dragged with fatigue, the Indians, very friendly now, offered to carry him. But Roger Williams assured them that he was not tired, only a little stiff.

Plumes of smoke, curling high above round bark lodges, apprised Roger that they were at last nearing the Indian village, and a few minutes' walk disclosed the camp in a shallow valley, surrounded by giant fir trees. Children and dogs, gamboling in the snow, ran to greet the newcomer with a noisy welcome. The two Indians led the white man to the oblong lodge in the center of the camp. It was larger than the round lodges and stood a little apart. Roger found himself suddenly in a smoke-filled room, hung with mats and trays woven of grass. All he could see for a moment was a fitful fire in the center of the floor, and smoke curling upward to the hole in the roof. He made out presently the painted savage face, topped by a feather headdress, staring at him. The Sachem was sitting before the fire, stiff and motionless, smoking a pipe. The two Indians began to talk very fast. Roger pulled out a string of colored beads from his knapsack, and bowing low, presented it to the chief.

"You come alone? You are not afraid?" asked Massasoit, accepting the gift graciously.

"I trust God to care for me," replied Roger Williams quietly.

"That is good," nodded the chief. "Why do you bring that?" he demanded, pointing at the gun.

"Wolves: I heard them all the while," explained Roger.

Massasoit smiled and nodded, and exclaimed suddenly, "I remember you, I know you, you are a friend in Plymouth."

"A friend," Roger assured him earnestly.

"Why did you come?" asked Massasoit.

"I came to become better acquainted. I want to learn your language better," Roger answered cautiously.

A wide smile spread over Massasoit's face now. He lifted his hand and invited the white man to sit down beside him, and offered him a pipe. Roger sat down stiffly, accepted the pipe and puffed in silence. Massasoit plied him with questions. He must make answers, he must talk. His head drooped, he loosened his stiff damp cloak, and let it fall from his shoulders, and tried to satisfy the chieftain's curiosity. His eyes closed, his head bobbed. He fell asleep at last.

He awakened to the sound of an Indian chant. He sat bolt upright. Where was he? It was dark in the lodge now, the fire was banked low for the night. He could see all around him, in the darkness, a number of Indians and squaws, stretched out on mats on slightly raised platforms, naked, excepting for loincloths, and bearskins only partly covered them. He felt ravenously hungry.

Massasoit leaned over him. "Nothing to eat this night. Tomorrow we go hunt and eat."

Roger nodded, understanding. Rations were lean in winter. He marveled that the Sachem received him so willingly. All night the Indians kept up their chant, and Roger realized at last that it was a prayer for good hunting tomorrow. The vermin, meanwhile, feasted freely on them all, especially on the white man.

The winter months went by slowly. The men went hunting every day, while the women did the chores. They chopped wood, fetched water, ground corn for bread, baked and cooked, and made mats and pots out of bark and dried grass. Roger went hunting with the men. Once they came upon a bear, lodged for the winter in a hollow under a tree. They poked him with poles, made of saplings and when he came out, shot him and carried him home. There was a great feast that day; everyone was welcome.

Roger Williams was learning something new about the Indians every day. They could laugh at small jokes, they were eager to share food with anyone, and they listened to him with deep attention when he offered to teach them as they sat by the fire of an evening.

He was learning their language, and writing down sentences on pieces of bark. Some day, he promised himself, he would write a grammar of their language so that the white man could learn to understand them more easily. But he knew all the while, nevertheless, that one wrong word or gesture might cost him his scalp.

"Tell us more about your God," Massasoit asked him often.

"God made everything," explained Roger. "The world and everything in it, and He gave us good laws to live by. All good things are from God." He recited the commandments and explained their meaning in simple words.

Massasoit nodded solemnly. "We believe the same," he said. "Our God is in everything, the sea and the sky. We call him Kaatian. I like your God. Tell me more about Jesus. Is it true he made sick people well, and told warriors to love their enemies?"

Roger Williams was getting accustomed to the smoke-filled lodges, the bad smells, the sleepless nights, and vermin. And he was finding out how much easier it was to teach great truths to childlike minds than to the learned ministers at the Bay. But he was glad when the snow began to melt and run in rivulets into pools around the camp. He could take expeditions with Massasoit now and look for a likely site to build a home for his family.

One day, much to the excitement of the children playing in puddles and squaws weaving mats in their lodges, a white man appeared in the village. Everyone came out, as he stopped to inquire for Roger Williams. "You friend?" The squaws showed white teeth, and let him wait and watch the children at play.

Roger Williams was both surprised and pleased to see William Harris waiting for him when he came back that afternoon. He had found a site on the Seekonuck River. Massasoit offered it to him as a present. They had made a bargain; Roger accepted the gift, and made a promise for a proper gift in return. "Do you bring news about Mary and the children?" he asked eagerly.

"They are well, and thriving," Harris assured him. "Mary is waiting for you to send for them."

"It will be soon now," confided Roger. "I have found just the place for us—not too far away from our people, and near enough to my Indian friends where I can help them."

"I have come to join you, if you will let me," announced Harris. "I am weary of the Bay and their laws."

A few days later the miller from Dorchester arrived at the camp, and told Roger that the Elders had banished him also.

Massasoit listened to their conversation and smiled craftily. The white men talked about their God who gave them good laws to live by, but they quarreled among themselves. He couldn't comprehend this. He was even more puzzled when two other white men appeared and asked Roger to let them share in his adventure.

Seekonuck seemed a fair place: fields, woods, a river. The five men busied themselves, breaking soil for planting and felling timber for building. They worked and sang. Soon they would be able to send for their families. And then, late one afternoon, an Indian arrived with a message from Winslow of Plymouth. " . . . Remove but to the other side of the water . . ." he wrote "ye will be free of the Bay and of Plymouth, and we will be loving neighbors."

It was hard to abandon plowed fields and cabins they had started to build, but it would be harder still to remain and be under the coercion of the Elders. They packed their belongings into a canoe and set forth, bound for they knew not where.

It was a fair day, the sky sparkled, adventure lay ahead; who knew what tomorrow would bring? The men took turns with the paddles. They were young, they sang their songs again, and scanned the scraggly banks of the other side of the water. Suddenly a cheerful hail rang out from one of the overhanging slate rocks—"What cheer, Netap [friend]?" Looking up, Roger recognized an Indian he had traded with at Salem. He called back a greeting, and climbed up to the ledge to take counsel with him.

"Go to the southward," advised the brave. "You'll find there a point where two fair rivers empty into the salty water."

The sun was still high, but the long spring twilight would soon begin. The prospectors paddled with renewed zeal.

A band of Indians were cooking their dinner when the white men arrived at last, at the point of the two rivers. The red men came running to the boat to welcome the strangers, and invited them to share their boiled bass and succotash.

The food tasted good to the hungry men. But Roger Williams remained standing, taking a swift survey of the panorama before him, marveling at the beauty of it. To the west lay a sheltered cove; a tidal waterway ran past southward, broadening gradually into the great Narragansett Bay, and he knew that the sea was not many miles away. Fields for planting and meadows for grazing cattle stretched as far as the eye could see. And high above the cove towered a wooded hillside to shelter homes they would build.

"This is Providence," he exclaimed. "This is Providence of the Most Holy and Wise." He walked about, poking into clam beds on the shore, and noting that the rivers were full of fish. Yes, this was Providence; a fair harbor, not only for himself and his companions,

but for countless other seekers like him. "Who is the Sachem?"
he went now to ask the Indians.

"Cononicus is the Sachem and Mionotonomo, his nephew," the
Indians told him with pride. "Cononicus, much big chief."

"Cononicus?" exclaimed Roger in a delighted voice. "I know
Cononicus; he came to my trading post at Salem many times."

The elderly Sachem received the white men with a warm welcome when they found his lodge early the next morning.

"Sell us land, and we will be good neighbors," proposed Roger
Williams, after the greetings were over, and they had smoked the
pipes offered them.

Cononicus puffed in silence for a while and nodded solemnly.

It did not take long to settle the bargain. Roger Williams took
care to write out a deed. Cononicus signed it with the mark of a
bow and Mionotonomo made the mark of an arrow.

They were neighbors now. The Indians sold them seed to plant
fields: corn, pumpkin, beans, squash. They had a will to work.

Trees were felled and fields planted. Roger Williams commis-
sioned an agent to mortgage his property at Salem and bought tools.
They helped each other build their houses. Hammering could be
heard from early dawn till dark. The Indians came to watch them
with curiosity and good will.

Would Mary like the little house on the cove with the river
tumbling past the door? Roger wrote her a description of the
houses they were building—a "fire" room on the first floor, and a
bedroom on the upper floor.

Mary could hardly believe her eyes when she arrived at last with
her two small daughters and her household treasures. She looked
upon the little house nestling in the cove, the tall hills above, great
trees brooding in a deep silence, and the river talking in a whisper,
making promises of who knew what. "It is a paradise," she cried
out, "a veritable paradise."

Seven years had gone by. The camp Roger Williams named
Providence, had become a refuge for the oppressed and discontented. There were now four small towns in Providence Planta-

tions; cattle browsed in meadows, fields yielded abundant harvests, and there was a mill for grinding corn.

The hard lean years were over. Roger and Mary had more children now, and a larger house. The Indians liked to come there often. They came to trade, and remained to visit. Mary kept open house; she entertained Indian chiefs and distinguished scholars with equal hospitality. It was a happy household; it rang with children's voices, Indian talk, and also with wise discourses, and plans of things to come.

Once in a while, Mary liked to take stock of all that had happened to them, and to marvel at her husband. He, who was a Cambridge scholar, traded with Indians, plowed fields, and did a yeoman's work as if he were born to it.

But Roger Williams was taking his chores for granted. His main thoughts remained preoccupied with the great purpose of his life. He was making a brave experiment, shaping a government after his own ideal. In Providence, every man was free to worship as he chose: Baptist, Quaker, Jew, Catholic. There was but one officer in Providence, and his only duty was to call a meeting once a fortnight to settle questions of land and planting. They settled these questions by mutual consent, and in peaceful discussions. Every householder had a right to vote; every married man became a householder. If a newcomer had no means to buy land, he worked and earned the thirty shillings required to buy a plot. There was but one rule enjoined on them all: that there be no evil done to any.

"Are you happy?" Mary asked him now and then when they took time to talk a while after a busy day. "You have given up the society of learned men and fair ways of living. Are you content?"

His friend, Winslow of Plymouth, had asked him this very question after a visit to Providence. Had Winslow understood the answer he wrote him? Perhaps only he, himself, he realized, could fully understand what he had gained in return for what he had given up. He tried to answer Mary's questions in a simpler way—"I have come a long distance across a wide ocean in order that I might proclaim freedom to worship God in a spirit of love, holiness and meekness, unmolested by vain doctrines; here, in Providence, we have no persecution for cause of conscience. This one thing I have gained, and more."

"The Elders of the Bay call Providence a sewer for the poor and discontented," reminded Mary.

"Ay, the Elders do not like our ways," agreed Roger Williams with a wry smile. "Nevertheless, it has proven to be a good way. We have no discontented here, no poor, no idlers."

But he did not want to think about the Elders now. They were still pursuing him with animosity, though it was he who had stopped the Pequot Indians from making war on the Bay Colony. The Elders had quickly forgotten how he had gone to the Pequots, at their request, to induce the savages to stop making preparations for war. He had remained with the Pequots for many days. He had risked his own life; the Indians were in no mood to reason. They had suffered many wrongs and were at last determined to wipe the white men out. It took many days and many nights, and it took much courage to persuade the angry savages to talk of peace, for they were determined to attack. The chieftains listened to him at last, out of their trust in him, and renewed treaties of peace. But no sooner was the danger over than the Elders began to plot, and to assert that he, Roger Williams, had no title to Providence.

"The Elders will not let you set foot in the Bay Colony," brooded Mary, as if guessing his thoughts. "They have forgotten that you risked your life to save them from a massacre."

"I would do it again," said Roger, quietly. "It was not merely to save them, though I would do that also."

But what were words, only dim images of what unfolded slowly in the storehouse of his thoughts. Providence was but a beginning, a small pattern for free men. He fell into a deep silence, thinking his thoughts. . . . The pattern would grow and become clearer. Strong men of good will would embellish it, and nurture it in a great faith, and sacrifice their worldly goods, even as he had sacrificed ambition, and privilege of worldly ways, in order that he might kindle a spark to light the way to a brighter, free world.

PATRICK HENRY

—— 1765 ——

*"I know not what course others may take; but as for
me, give me liberty, or give me death!"*

IT WAS EARLY MORNING. THE SUN WAS SHINING AND
birds were singing in the gnarled old oak tree on the bank of the
river. The water ran so smoothly and quietly, you could hardly
hear it. A man in a coonskin cap was sitting under the oak tree
fishing. He listened to the birds and to the river, and watched the
silver trout under the water, but his thoughts were far away. His
tall shaggy horse nibbled at the grass nearby and waited patiently.
He was hungry and the grass was mostly weeds, but he was used
to that and he seemed not to mind it.

An old wagon rumbled down the road and slowed up. The man in the wagon looked around and waved his hand. But the fisherman was not looking in his direction and did not see him. The man in the wagon shook his head, and clucked to his horse to go on. He was in a hurry to get to the store, to trade the pelt of the fox he had trapped on his mountain farm, for nails he needed to fix his roof.

"I saw Patrick Henry fishing," he told the storekeeper, later.

"I thought Patrick went to Williamsburg to sit in the House of Burgesses," exclaimed a wiry little man sorting seeds he wanted for his garden.

"So did I," said the farmer. "But there he was sitting on the bank of the South Anna fishing."

"Maybe Louisa County made a mistake to elect Patrick to the House," said the little man.

"Maybe so," said the farmer. "Patrick failed as a storekeeper and he failed as a farmer. He may fail as a politician."

The storekeeper shook his head. Everybody in Hanover came to his store to buy and to trade, and stayed to talk about this one and that one. "Folks think well of Patrick," he said at last. "Patrick is a good lawyer."

"Patrick studied law only six weeks," laughed the little man.

"He is a mighty good lawyer," said the storekeeper again. "He won that 'Parson's Cause' case right over lawyer Lyons head. People are expecting big things of Patrick."

A rider in buckskin breeches and a coonskin cap over his tousled red hair, pulled up his horse at the door at this moment, and entered the store, carrying a fishing basket over his shoulder. "Good morning," he called out in a friendly voice.

"Good morning, Patrick Henry," said the storekeeper. "We thought maybe you went to Williamsburg."

"I should be on my way there now," admitted Patrick. "But there isn't a better place to think things over than sitting with a fishing rod in your hand and a fish nibbling at the bait."

The men crowded around the newcomer to examine the silvery trout shining against the sides of the basket.

"I'll trade you a new rod for the catch," offered the storekeeper.

"I guess Sally will want half of it," smiled Patrick. "And you take the rest."

The storekeeper went to fetch a basket to transfer his share of the fish while Patrick scanned the shelf. "It isn't a fishing rod I want this morning, but a little present to leave with my wife and the children while I am away to Williamsburg," he said after a while. His eyes fell on a crock of wild honey on the counter, as he spoke. "That's just the thing," he nodded.

"Jim Hastings found a honey tree the other day. It's the best honey I've had in a long while," said the storekeeper, measuring off a generous chunk of golden honey into a container.

Patrick fitted the small crock of honey into the pocket of his hunting jacket, flung the basket of fish to his shoulder and rode away as suddenly as he had come. Humming a tune and weighing in his mind the things he had been thinking about when fishing, he hardly noticed how his horse galloped to get home to breakfast.

"Father is coming, Mother!" Little Martha ran shouting into the house where Sally was preparing her spinning wheel for the day. Sally and her two younger daughters, Ann and Betsy, came out on the porch where Billy, the young terrier was barking a wild welcome at his master. Patrick lifted his little daughters, one after the other, for a swing high above his shoulders. They screamed and laughed, and asked to do it again.

"What?" he cried, pretending to be angry. "Away with you. You are making me work too hard." But they knew he was only pretending and that he would swing them again. They laughed and danced about him and hung on to his hunting jacket.

"I nearly forgot to tell you in this commotion," said Patrick, "I bumped right into a honey tree."

"A honey tree?" shouted little Martha.

"A honey tree, a honey tree," sang the little girls reaching for the crock of honey.

"Help, help," cried Patrick capturing the crock, and handing it to Sally. "The honey tree sent it to you with compliments."

Sally laughed, and took the honey jar. "We were waiting breakfast for you," and she led the family to the belated breakfast.

They gathered around the table and listened wide eyed to Patrick's account of his adventure—"Shandy, the horse, found a four-leaf clover in the weeds. The birds were so pleased they began to sing a dance tune, and would you believe it, the trout in the brook danced to the tune." The little girls shouted with delight. They were used to his stories. But suddenly he stopped talking, got up from the table and began to pack a bundle, to take with him to Williamsburg: a homespun coat and a fresh shirt to wear to the House of Burgesses. "They will be elegant folks there," he said to Sally, pointing with pretended disapproval at the hunting shirt he was wearing.

"They may be dressed in elegant coats, but you'll measure up to the best of them," said Sally with confidence.

"Play us a tune, father," begged little Martha.

"Yes, yes, play us a tune," chimed in Ann and Betsy.

"Who ever heard of it, a tune so early in the morning?" Patrick pretended to look outraged.

"A good-by tune," said little Martha.

"I'll play you a weepy tune then," said Patrick, brushing away imaginary tears.

"A dance tune, father, a merry tune," cried the little girls clapping their hands.

"So? A dance tune? Very well," he said, still pretending to weep. His fiddle in his hands now, he began to play one tune after another. The children danced around him in circles, singing the tunes to keep time. Then his face became stern. He stopped playing, laid the fiddle in its case and tied it into his bundle.

Jack White, his young Negro servant, brought the shaggy horse to the door now.

"There," cried Patrick, "Jack knows I should be on my way."

"Must you go? Do you have to go away?" The little girls clung to his legs and to his arms.

"Be good, be extra good while I am away." He lifted each one for another high swing and a kiss.

Sally walked beside him to where the impatient horse was pawing the ground, eager to be off.

"There will be important questions to decide," said Patrick quietly.

"You will be equal to whatever comes up," Sally assured him.

He leaned over, kissed her good-by, and jumped on his horse. The young terrier ran barking after him as the horse trotted away.

The sun was high in the blue sky, the air was sweet with honeysuckle and wild orange. It was a beautiful morning. Patrick Henry sat on his horse, lost in thought. He had not been in Williamsburg since the day he went there to ask Wythe and Peyton Randolph to sign his license to practice law. He smiled now as he remembered it all—Wythe, the learned scholar, refused even to listen to his arguments.

"You say you studied law alone, and only for six weeks?" asked Wythe with a frown. "Go to college, young man, and study with proper teachers," he told him.

It was a great good fortune for him, mused Patrick, that the venerable Peyton Randolph became interested in his arguments and consented to sign his license to practice law. And two other lawyers did likewise. They believed in him. Why? wondered Patrick, gratefully. He promised them that he would continue to read and to study. But that was not the reason they believed in him; he understood it better now. They were convinced he could be a lawyer by the way he argued his own case with them. "Yes," he cried aloud, and the lean horse under him bounced forward to a quicker pace, raising a cloud of red dust on the bumpy road. "I proved it, I proved I am a good lawyer."

The sun was hot on his shoulders. Patrick took off his cap and mopped his forehead. He felt excited and happy and a little uneasy at the same time. He was going to sit in the House of Burgesses. It was an honor, but more important, he thought soberly, was the opportunity he would now have to help shape events, make changes for the better for the people in the colonies.

It was dusk by the time his horse turned into Duke of Gloucester Street. After Hanover, Williamsburg seemed very elegant to Patrick. Fashionable ladies in silks and velvets passed him by in elegant carriages. Patrick galloped down the entire length of the street from William and Mary College at one end, to the Capitol at the other. He turned about to trot back to the Raleigh Tavern. The uncurtained windows of the tavern sparkled with candlelight. Patrick reined his horse, and watched the parade of gentlemen in powdered wigs, frilled shirts, velvet coats and knee breeches, coming and going in and out of the wide doors of the tavern. It would be a pleasant place to stay the night, but as he jingled his meager purse in his hand, he decided he must find himself a cheaper place. He thought of Sally and his little daughters snug at home. He felt lonely now, wondering where he could find a bed to sleep.

Two men came out of the tavern talking and laughing, and stopped to try a new dance step on the green in front of the tavern. Patrick pulled his violin out of his bundle and started to play a dance tune. A horseman galloped by, and came back presently. A tall slender young man with sandy red hair leaned forward from the saddle—"Patrick Henry," he called out in a surprised voice. "I was wondering who it could be, playing like that."

"Thomas Jefferson," exclaimed Patrick in a delighted voice.

"What are you doing in Williamsburg?" asked Jefferson.

"I guess you haven't heard I've been elected to the House of Burgesses from Louisa County," said Patrick with a slow smile.

"Then you've come to Williamsburg to sit in the House of Burgesses. Stay the night at my house," invited Jefferson.

"Thank you," said Patrick with a wide smile. "I was just wondering where I'd sleep this night."

"I'll hurry and tell Caesar there will be company, and you come along," Jefferson called over his shoulder as he galloped away in the dusk.

Patrick finished playing his tune, and went to find a stable to put his horse away for the night.

Caesar, Jefferson's young slave, was waiting for him at the door when he arrived, the bundle under his arm. "Come right in, sir, come right in." Caesar beamed a wide smile as he led the way into Jefferson's bachelor apartment. It was a pleasant room to come into out of the night. Candles were lit on the fine mahogany table. The white cloth and the silver sparkled in the candlelight. Book shelves crowded with books lined the walls: law books, histories, poetry. Patrick put his bundle on the sofa, took off his coonskin cap, and went to wash the dust from his hands and face.

Jefferson came in from an inner room now, his sandy hair freshly combed, his white face shining with a genial smile. He was seven years younger that Patrick, and he was still a student, studying law at William and Mary College, but already he was a finished gentleman. "You are just in time," he exclaimed gaily. "Caesar is waiting to give us our supper."

The cold meat and hot corn bread tasted good to Patrick after his long ride. There were many things to talk about, pleasant things they both remembered as they sat in the soft candlelight—"Do you remember the first time we met?" asked Jefferson in his slow genial voice. "Twas a house party at Captain Daindridge's house."

"Ay, at Hanover, at Captain Nathaniel West Daindridge's house. It was Christmas holiday," reminisced Patrick with a wide smile.

"I still remember the dance tunes you played," smiled Jefferson. "But I hear you have become a great lawyer now," he added, shortly.

"I wouldn't claim that." Patrick looked very serious now, and pleased at the same time, that Jefferson had heard a flattering report of him.

"The learned lawyers, here in Williamsburg, talk with much wonder of the way you pleaded that 'Parson's Cause' case," said Jefferson.

"The lawyers are surprised I won the case, because they know I studied by myself, and only for six weeks," grinned Patrick.

"Well, yes," admitted Jefferson. "It's a wonder to us all; and what's more to wonder at is that you win every case you take."

"The 'Parson's Cause' case was my first case," said Patrick. "I was mighty anxious to win that case for my clients. I read and studied in the law books, and prepared my case carefully to make sure my arguments would be correct. But first I made sure I was in the right. When I know a thing is right, I plead from the heart."

"From the heart, I like that," exclaimed Jefferson. "Maybe you didn't need to read law books as long as we all do at college."

"As to that, I promised Peyton Randolph when he signed my

license that I would read and study, and I do," said Patrick.

"When you are not fishing and hunting," laughed Jefferson.

"It is true, I'd rather fish and hunt," confessed Patrick with a wide smile. Caesar came in now to clear the table. Jefferson took his violin from the top shelf of his bookcase and began to tune it.

"That 'Parson's Cause' case," said Patrick, "gave me a chance to show the Parliament in England that they can't tell us here in the colonies, what we should pay our clergy. The Parliament in England is running us high handed, what with taxes and trade regulations."

"That's true," Jefferson nodded, his face clouded now. "But we can't deny that England has a right to tax her colonies and that's what we are, a colony to England."

"Nevertheless, they go too far, and now there is that Stamp Act. It's not only a nuisance, but a hardship," cried Patrick, with such heat that Jefferson stopped tuning his violin, and stood waiting to hear what he had on his mind. "We'll have to pay for a stamp every time we use a legal paper, and every time we buy a newspaper or sign a document. Are we going to submit to that?"

Jefferson scratched a few notes on his violin, his face grave and thoughtful. He felt embarrassed that he had not given the question much thought. Patrick seemed to know and to understand things he had hardly thought about. "No one likes the Stamp Act, but what can we do about it?" he asked after a while.

Patrick fumbled in his bundle for his violin and struck up one of the tunes they had played together at the Christmas house party in Hanover. It was a merry tune; they broke out into a song, and began to dance. Another tune came to their minds, and then another. They forgot England, and the tax and law books. Their voices rang out through the windows into the starlit night. Suddenly there was a loud banging on the door. Jefferson stopped playing and went to the door still holding the fiddle in his hand. A man in a nightshirt and a night cap over his head was shivering in the night air on the doorstep.

"Sir," he cried indignantly. "The whole neighborhood is waiting for you to stop fiddling. It is long past midnight. No one can sleep with such noise going on."

"I am right sorry, sir," apologized Jefferson. "I had no idea it was that late."

"Look at the clock, look at the clock," roared the man, as he turned to go to his house.

Jefferson tiptoed back into his rooms and went to bed. Patrick took off his dusty boots and curled up on the sofa to sleep.

The sun was just rising when Patrick wakened. This was the *day,* he remembered instantly, his first day to sit in the House of Burgesses. He tiptoed noiselessly into the dressing room to wash and dress himself with particular care.

When Jefferson wakened a little later, he saw Patrick sitting at the window dressed in the new homespun coat he had brought with him, his red unruly hair carefully groomed. He was too engrossed, writing on the flyleaf of an old book, to notice Jefferson standing in the doorway.

"I hope you don't mind," he called out when he looked up presently and saw Jefferson watching him with an amused smile.

"Not in the least," Jefferson assured him. "The book is in tatters."

"I didn't want to waken you to ask for paper," explained Patrick, as he tore the leaf from the book, folded it carefully, and put it in his pocket.

Caesar came in with breakfast now, and Jefferson wondered what Patrick had to write down in such a hurry that he couldn't wait to ask for paper. But Patrick Henry didn't offer to tell him.

The Capitol building was crowded to the door for there were many people in Williamsburg who were anxious to hear the debate on the Stamp Act. The law students from William and Mary College were obliged to stand in the doorway to listen to the discourses in the House of Burgesses. Patrick lingered in the entrance for a parting word with Jefferson before he pushed his way through the crowd into the courtroom. Speaker of the House Robinson, was already in his place at the front. The leaders of the House, wealthy plantation owners in powdered wigs and broadcloth coats, were talking in little clusters, laughing at each other's pleasantries.

They didn't seem at all preoccupied with the important question that was to be discussed, marveled Patrick Henry. He was glad to recognize George Johnston, of Fairfax County, standing near by. Here was someone he could sound out—"What will be done about the Stamp Act, sir?" he asked Johnston.

"Nothing more can be done about it," Johnston shrugged his shoulders. "The Stamp Act's been passed. We don't like it, but what can we do about it?" he demanded.

"We can protest," cried Patrick hotly.

"Protest?" Johnston looked surprised.

"If we accept the Stamp Act without a protest it's a sign we've no spirit. That's what they'll think about us in England, and they'll be right. And they'll levy more taxes on us. We'll be taxed and taxed and taxed again and again."

"We have no redress. We can't stop them taxing us. We're subject to the crown," reasoned Johnston.

Patrick pulled out a folded paper from his pocket and handed it to Johnston. "I've written out seven resolutions, sir, if you would care to read them. You might be willing also to second them."

Johnston took the paper and read it slowly. An excited look came into his eyes. "I'm with you, sir, I'll second your resolutions," he cried.

Speaker Robinson was now pounding the table with his silver mace. Patrick slouched into his seat on the long wooden bench with the other burgesses. Two men on the bench beside him were talking in low grumbling voices. "We force the soil so as to grow bigger crops of tobacco so as to pay taxes to England," one of the men was saying.

"Ay, and if we keep on forcing the soil, there'll be no life left in it," said the other man. "It's getting poorer all the time."

"That's it," exclaimed a man in a nearby seat. "Can't raise crops on poor soil."

"I've no glass in my windows, but I must pay taxes to the crown before I spend money on window glass," broke in a third man.

"If we spent some of that tax money on fixing our roads—" mumbled another burgess from the up country.

"The meeting please come to order," cried the clerk.

A gentleman in a powdered wig and a handsome coat, stood up now and began to talk. He looked very imposing as he stood there, talking in a loud voice—"The Stamp Act seems to have caused much talk," he measured every word carefully. "The fact is, this tax is so small it is but a trifle. I see it more as a nuisance rather than a hardship to complain about."

"The cost of the stamp may be small, but it's an extra tax, and it's a tax too much," cried a voice from the back seat in the row of benches.

No one paid attention to the interruption. A stout man with many ruffles of fine lace on his shirt stood up now and began to explain the reason why the colonies should pay the tax with good grace—"The English Parliament deems it necessary to fix the Stamp Act, therefore we, the loyal subjects to the crown, are willing to obey."

"The two gentlemen hold the welfare of the crown before the welfare of the colonies, it seems to me," Patrick whispered to Johnston.

"Governor Fauquier is a Tory as you may have heard, and he has many admirers in the House," Johnston whispered back.

Patrick listened to the speeches of the leaders of the House with a frown, and shifted uneasily in his seat. Suddenly he stood up and began to talk. His voice sounded frightened at the first few words:

"The English Parliament is interfering with the affairs of the colonies," he exclaimed. "The misrule of the English Parliament has brought great hardships to the colonies," Patrick's voice grew louder and firmer.

"Who is this buckskin gentleman, giving his views?" cried an indignant voice from the front.

"An ignorant fellow from the backwoods," said one of the lawyers with a shrug.

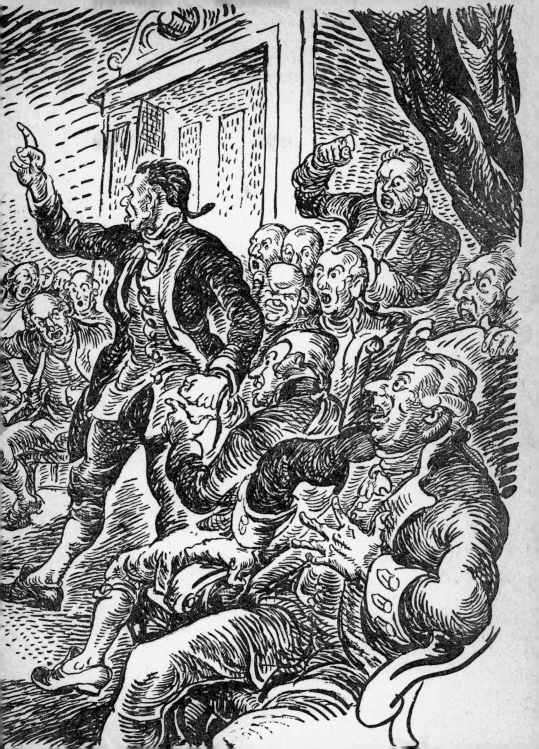

Patrick went on talking as if he had not heard them. He was talking about something he understood and treasured. He was talking about liberty, the right of men to govern themselves. His eyes glowed, his voice rang. A spell fell on the assembly as they listened to his arguments—"We submit to taxation without representation," he cried in a challenging voice.

Peyton Randolph frowned. He was a proud Virginia gentleman, and he was also attorney general to the king of England.

"This thing must be stopped," he said to Pendleton. Wythe shook his head. A debate started up now as leaders of the House rose to interrupt Patrick at every word—"Is this new member from Louisa County claiming Virginia has a right to make laws to resist the English Parliament?" demanded an indignant voice.

In answer Patrick unfolded the piece of paper he was holding in his hand and began to read what he had scribbled there early that morning:

"The first adventurers who settled in America brought with them the right of franchise," Patrick pronounced each word in a high fiery voice.

"What's that?" interrupted an angry man at the front. Patrick straightened his shoulders and went on reading from his paper, explaining the rights of the colonies.

"Two royal charters were granted by King James the First that entitled the colonies to all privileges, liberties and immunities . . . as if they were living within the realm of England . . ."

"Patrick Henry may be from the backwoods," called out a burgess from the benches, "but it's Patrick Henry, this man from the backwoods, and not our learned lawyers who is saying what we need to know."

"Yes, that's true," said Wythe to Peyton Randolph. "I now wish I had signed his license to practice law."

Peyton Randolph frowned, his face red and angry.

"Resolved therefore," Patrick went on—"Resolved that the general assembly of this colony have the only sole and exclusive rights and power to lay taxes and impositions upon the inhabitants of this colony."

"This is sedition," cried out a Tidewater gentleman.

"Sedition, sedition," cried out several leaders of the House.

"No person that is not in the general assembly of the colonies has a right to impress taxation on the people of the colonies; such a person should be considered an enemy. Caesar had his Brutus and Charles the Second his Cromwell and George the Third—"

"Shame, shame," interrupted the Speaker of the House, pounding his mace on the table.

"Treason," cried an indignant voice. "Shame, treason, treason," resounded from all sides.

Patrick looked around him slowly, noting the frightened faces. His eyes flashed—"And George the Third may profit by their example." His voice rang and echoed in the ceiling. "If this be treason, make the most of it."

The whole House buzzed with excited voices now. The burgesses crowded around Patrick to congratulate him, clapping him on the shoulder, shaking his hand.

"Who was Caesar?" a farmer was asking.

"Caesar was a dictator in olden times in Rome. He ruled the people of Rome without their consent exactly, and Brutus killed him. And Charles the Second tried to rule England without Parliament; Cromwell and his army beheaded him," explained a more informed burgess with a knowing wink.

At the front of the House, Tidewater gentlemen were talking in troubled voices. Many of them agreed with what Patrick said, but they were not ready to say aloud what might bring on war.

Patrick listened to the buzz of many voices all talking at once. There was to be a vote. They were going to vote on his resolves. The burgesses from the back country were in high spirits, making jokes and laughing. They gave their vote fearlessly; come what might, they were ready for it in their own minds. Patrick listened to the vote as it was taken— Some of the burgesses had gone home to their mountain farms to look after the spring plowing, but there were enough left who would vote for his resolves. "We'll win by a small majority," he whispered to Johnston. He looked very sober now. Virginia must not lose this chance to stand up, and show the

English Parliament that the colonies had a spirit in them to resist oppression.

The clerk cleared his throat and announced the vote. The resolves had passed. That meant that the colonies would offer a protest based on what they knew was their right.

The House adjourned. The burgesses could go home now to their plowing. They lingered a while to talk— This was an important day. They all only dimly guessed how important it was. They left the Capitol at last. There was a lot to think about on the way home. This day, May 29, 1765, was a day to remember.

Patrick went now to find his bundle which he had left in a corner of the entry.

"You spoke with courage and with wisdom." Jefferson came up now to press his hand warmly. "From today, I shall take note of the affairs in the colonies."

"You spoke for all Virginia," one of the leaders of the House stopped to say to Patrick as he was leaving the Capitol.

"I hope so, sir," Patrick bowed. He could bow with as much grace as any Tidewater gentleman when he chose. But now he was thinking of going home. He went to get his horse. He could go fishing with an easy mind now, and he might hunt in the woods, and trap a bear, as he once did— But his foremost thought would remain with meetings in Louisa County, and in the Hanover Court-house, where he would raise his voice to challenge men's minds to think of freedom as a gift already theirs to claim.

His lean horse trotted briskly over the red clay road. Patrick clicked his tongue to spur him on. He was in a hurry to get home to share his happiness with Sally. He had spoken for Virginia. He felt proud of that, but in the back of his thoughts was the hope that all the other colonies might hear of it, and arise to speak for their rights.

SAMUEL ADAMS

—— 1773 ——

*"If we suffer tamely a lawless attack upon our liberty,
we encourage it, and involve others in our doom."*

MR. NATHANIEL ALLAN LOOKED OUT OF THE WIN-
dow of his warehouse and frowned. Boston streets had been in
a turmoil for the last few days. Farmers from the outlying country, mechanics and ship workers, rough-looking men, crowded the
walks; one could hardly go anywhere without bumping into one
of them.

"There's trouble brewing again," he said to Mr. Billings, his book-keeper.

"I guess Samuel Adams sent out one of his circular letters," said Mr. Billings, pushing his thick glasses to the top of his forehead. "Every time Samuel Adams wants to make trouble, he sends out a circular letter to farmers and mechanics, and they flock to Boston to listen to his complaints against Britain." Mr. Billings mopped his pale thin face with his handkerchief, and adjusted the glasses on his narrow nose with a self-righteous smile.

Mr. Allan's young nephew, Robert, glanced up from the letter he was writing, and made a wry face. He disliked the way Mr. Billings smiled. "Doddard," he muttered and lifted his tow head higher. "Maybe it's true that Samuel Adams is a very smart man," he said aloud.

These words were like an explosion of a gun in Mr. Allan's ears. His ruddy face grew purple under his white powdered wig. "What's that you said?" he demanded in a voice that trembled with anger.

Robert smoothed his thick thatch of blond hair with both hands and hesitated a moment. A defiant look came into his young face.

"I've heard lots of people say that Samuel Adams is a smart man. Only yesterday, I heard Dr. Thomas Young and John Hancock talking on Griffin's wharf. Dr. Young said, 'Samuel Adams is a great man.' I heard him say it," insisted Robert.

"Thomas Young is a Whig, a 'Son of Liberty,' a 'Patriot,' he calls himself, and so is John Hancock, more the pity. Rebels, that's what they are, and you had better mind your own business. A loyal Tory doesn't listen to Whigs' orations."

Mr. Billings snickered, and glanced at Robert. Should he tell Mr. Allan that he had seen Robert come out of Faneuil Hall only a few days ago, he wondered, and decided to keep the secret a while. If he told Mr. Allan today that Robert had been to one of those meetings of "The Sons of Liberty," listening to Samuel Adams, he'd go into a rage and make it unpleasant all day. He cleaned his glasses carefully, and said, "If those 'Sons of Liberty' begin to make trouble about the tea ships, Governor Hutchinson ought to lock Samuel Adams, and his entire secret club in jail."

Mr. Allan sighed and returned to his desk, a frown on his face.

"If Hutchinson were to put Samuel Adams in jail, there'd be a riot, and the whole mob would be after him. Hutchinson is too smart to tamper with these people unless Britain sends enough redcoats to back him; and that," he added gloomily, "might lead to war." But Mr. Allan did not want to talk about imaginary troubles just now. He went to the window again to stare at the two ships anchored off the wharf.

"If only the tea could be unloaded safely, there would be a handsome profit in that cargo. Britain is selling this excellent tea to the colonies for half the price people in London are paying for it."

Mr. Billings watched Mr. Allan and made calculations on a pad of paper. It was no secret that the East India Tea Company owed Britain money and had tried to pay off its debt with tea. The warehouses in London were loaded with East India Tea, and that tea had to be sold for cash. That way the East India Company would pay its debt. That was the reason Britain was selling this tea to the colonies for half price. "A very excellent idea," mumbled Mr. Billings, biting at his quill. "Everybody would benefit: the colonies would get good tea cheap, the tea company would pay its debts, and Britain would be rid of the unwanted tea. Why then is old Samuel Adams making trouble about it? The tax on the tea is small enough!"

Robert finished the letter, and carried it to Mr. Allan's desk.

"I'll read it later," said Mr. Allan still busy with his thoughts.

Outdoors, there was a din of whistles blowing and voices shouting. Robert opened the door softly and went out.

Where were all these people going, he wondered, pushing his way through the crowded streets. On King Street he saw a placard nailed to a tree and stopped to read it: ". . . Friends, Brethren, Countrymen. . . . Every friend to his country, to himself and to posterity is now called upon to meet at Faneuil Hall. . . ." This was a call from Samuel Adams, guessed Robert. He had seen this placard for several days now. A queer looking duck was this Samuel Adams, thought Robert, thinking of the meeting he had attended a few days ago. Every time he became excited his hand shook with palsy, and his head bobbed. Robert stood thinking a moment, trying to remember what Samuel Adams had said that had made him feel so excited. Perhaps he was wrong, as his uncle said, to listen to him. For it did sound as if Samuel Adams were trying to make everybody believe that the Colonies could become a united and independent country. He made one want to fight for it. Robert decided to go to the meeting and find out more about it all.

The seats were all taken by the time he reached the hall. Robert leaned against the wall, and tried to follow what Samuel Adams was saying ". . . All men have a right to remain in a state of nature . . ." What does he mean? wondered Robert, noticing that the other people around him were listening intently and seemed to understand.

"The British rule interferes in our government. Though we are not represented in Parliament, yet we are taxed," explained a man standing close to Robert.

"I guess that's true," Robert whispered back, his face red.

"In case of intolerable oppression, civil or religious, men have a right to leave the society and enter another . . ." Samuel Adams thumped one hand on the other.

"That's sedition," hissed a voice near by.

Robert looked around uneasily, and recognized a friend of his uncle standing not far away, leaning on a gold-headed cane.

"We sent a declaration of our rights to Britain; the British Parliament had better heed it," Samuel Adams thumped his hands together again.

"I daresay it was none other than Sam himself who made up that declaration," exclaimed the man with the gold cane mockingly.

Several angry faces turned to glare at the Tory. Robert stole out of the hall. He did not want to get mixed up in a brawl. He walked swiftly towards Griffin's wharf. Why did his uncle want to be loyal to King George? he wondered. If the colonies became a free independent country, they would not be subject to any king. Did he have to be a Tory because his grandfather and his father had been Tories? He did not want to quarrel with his uncle, and he did not want to hurt his feelings. Robert tried to think it out, looking at both sides of the question, but the more he thought of it, the less clear it became to him.

A rough looking crowd of Boston citizens was on the wharf, keeping watch over the two ships, the *Eleanor* and the *Dartmouth;* a third ship, the *Beaver,* was still to arrive. Sailors were unloading cargo, talking and laughing noisily. "Are the sailors unloading the tea?" Robert asked one of the men.

"Let them just try," replied the man, toying with his gun.

"They are to unload all the cargo excepting tea," explained another man in a milder voice.

"And what then?" asked Robert, pretending he didn't know.

"We sent a petition to Governor Hutchinson to let the tea go back to Britain on the ships without unloading; he refused." The man spat on the floor and walked away.

"We've got twenty days," the captain of the *Dartmouth* was saying to a man in a white wig and silver shoe buckles. "Maybe the trouble'll blow over, and they'll let us unload the tea."

"They'll not give in," exclaimed a little man with sharp eyes —"A bad lot, armed with guns, there's not a gun left in any of the stores in Boston." He rubbed his hands and added, "The governor can't send the cargo back to Britain without a receipt from the customhouse, and the customhouse can't give a receipt until the tax is paid—that's the trouble," the man rubbed his hands again. "The Sons of Liberty gave notice the tea was not to be unloaded and the tax is not to be paid—they'd maybe burn the ships if we try to unload."

"If the tea is not unloaded by the time the twenty days are up, what will happen?" asked Robert eagerly.

"When the twenty days are up, the customhouse has a right to seize the ship," exclaimed the sharp eyed little man in a pleased voice.

The Tory in the powdered wig gave the little man a disdainful look.

"That's it, they'd seize the tea, and auction it off; and it would be bought by sharpers, and stored away in their warehouse and sold in secret for a good price, and who'd benefit?" he asked the captain, turning his back on the little speculator.

Robert left the wharf in a more uncertain state of mind than when he came there. Only one thing seemed clear to him: the "Sons of Liberty" were not thinking of any gain or profit for themselves; they talked only of the good of the colonies and the future of the people in the colonies, and they did not seem to be afraid of getting into trouble on account of it all. Why were they so set on not having the tea unloaded? he wondered. The tax was but a trifle. Why were they making such a fuss about it? He shrugged his shoulders. He would just forget about these people, he decided as he left the wharf. But the Tory's way of thinking made him feel uncomfortable now— He would wait and see what would happen, he told himself as he walked away.

It was a cold rainy evening in December. A log fire was burning cheerfully in the parlor of Nathaniel Allan's handsome house on Beacon Hill. Mrs. Allan was stitching at her embroidery near the fireplace. The lights from the candles, reflected in the gilt mirror over the mantel, shone on her dark silky head and on Mr. Allan's powdered wig and the gold snuff box on the small table at his side. Mr. Allan pretended to read the Boston Gazette, but he was watching Robert from the corner of his eye. Robert, slumped deep into his chair, was staring at his hands folded in his lap.

"Robert," Mr. Allan's voice crackled, and his paper shook in his hand. "Billings has been telling me that you've been to Faneuil Hall lately. I hope he is mistaken."

"I went there a few times," admitted Robert.

"No harm in that," interposed Mrs. Allan quietly.

"I forbid it," snapped Mr. Allan. "I forbid you to listen to those sons of sedition."

"I went to find out. I wanted to hear what they said so I would know for myself, so I would understand," stammered Robert.

"You wanted to hear what those traitors talk about? Sedition, that's what they're brewing. Once and for all, I forbid it," cried Mr. Allan outraged.

"Samuel Adams may be a queer fellow, and he may be homely to look at, his head bobbing and his arms shaking when he gets excited, but it's mighty interesting to listen to what he says," said Robert in a low rebellious voice, not daring to look at his uncle.

"Tell us what he said," exclaimed Mrs. Allan, more to comfort Robert than out of curiosity.

"I can't exactly remember," admitted Robert. "He said these colonies might become a great independent country, and Britain may some day come to us for favors and buy from us."

"Indeed," cried Mr. Allan, purple in the face with indignation. "He dares say it! A loyal Tory cannot listen to the seditious discourses of the Whigs."

"But if they talk about what is for the good of the colonies, and the good of the people of this continent? We surely ought to think about our rights and consider our interests," exclaimed Robert.

"Our interests are bound with Britain," snapped Mr. Allan. "I don't want you to forget that."

"I am eighteen years old. I am old enough to think," cried Robert.

"If you think sedition, you're a traitor to the king, and if you're a traitor to the king, you're a traitor to me," said Mr. Allan, trying to appear calm. "If you remain in my house and in my employ, you will have to think as I do."

"I only want to do what's right," said Robert, "I can't help thinking about what Samuel Adams said. If these colonies can become a great free country, I am for it."

"If that is the case, you are no longer in my employ. Don't let me see your face again unless you come to apologize, and to assure me you've changed your mind," shouted Mr. Allan.

Robert looked at Mrs. Allan. She was bending low over her embroidery, but he could see that she looked very frightened. He wanted to tell her not to worry about him, but he could not speak. He ran out of the room, and dashed up the stairs.

Mrs. Allan dropped her embroidery frame, and started to follow him to reason with him.

"Let him be, Lucy," cried Mr. Allan. "He'll come to his senses and apologize. That will be the end of the whole matter."

Robert made a small bundle of what he would take with him. He felt angry and frightened. He ran down the stairs and stood in the hall a moment longing to say good-by to Mrs. Allan, but he dreaded to face his uncle now. He opened the door and went out.

Mrs. Allan went to the window. She was crying, but she didn't want Mr. Allan to know it. She pulled the curtain aside and watched Robert as he trudged away in the rain.

"He'll come back and apologize. That will be the end of his folly," said Mr. Allan again, as he settled back in his chair to read the Boston Gazette.

It was very dark in the street—the lighted windows in the mansions on Beacon Hill made Robert feel very lonely. Now that he was on his own, where would he go? he wondered. He walked slowly peering into the lighted windows. Suddenly the door of John Hancock's mansion opened cautiously, and a man wrapped in a greatcoat came down the steps rapidly. Was it John Hancock? wondered Robert. If so, he was probably going to a secret meeting of the Sons of Liberty. Robert started to follow him, thinking of Samuel Adams; he wanted to hear him talk again. Perhaps then he would know what to do.

The man turned around suddenly. "What do you want?" he asked in a gruff voice.

It was John Hancock—"I want to join the Sons of Liberty," blurted out Robert, surprised at himself for saying this.

John Hancock eyed him sharply for a moment. "Aren't you the son of my neighbor, Nathaniel Allan?" he asked suspiciously.

"I am his nephew, sir," explained Robert.

"A Tory!—And you tell me you want to join the Sons of Liberty?" cried Mr. Hancock indignantly. "Spying for your uncle, I dare say."

"Indeed I'm not spying, sir," exclaimed Robert, taken aback. "Uncle Nathaniel is a Tory, that's true enough; but that doesn't make me a Tory. I told him that, and now I've left his house. In fact, I had to leave," added Robert in a shaking voice.

"I see," said John Hancock, walking slowly thinking it over. "You say you want to join the Sons of Liberty?"

"Yes, I do, sir," said Robert.

"Well then," said Mr. Hancock, "just follow me." He turned to knock on a shabby door of a rundown mansion which Robert knew belonged to William Molineaux. A slovenly servant opened the door, and let them enter, without asking any questions. John Hancock groped his way through the dark hall, past a dark parlor and walked up the stairs, lighted only by a small lamp on the upper floor. At the far end of the upper hall a buzz of men's voices could be heard. John Hancock tapped on the door softly; a burly man in a shaggy wig opened it a crack, and seeing Hancock let him enter the small room. A number of men were seated around a long table. John Hancock removed his coat, and sat down in the empty chair. "I forgot," he exclaimed in his loud jovial voice, "I brought a young friend with me." He went to the door and beckoned to Robert to enter.

Samuel Adams stopped talking and looked at Robert. His sallow face shone with a sudden smile. "We need all the young men we can get," his head bobbed.

Molineaux stared at Robert with absent eyes, and found a small bench for him in a corner.

"There's some talk that the two men of war in the harbor'll open fire to drive our guard from the wharf so the tea might be unloaded unbeknown to us," said Molineaux, wagging his shaggy head.

"Let them try. All Boston would be up in arms," exclaimed Samuel Adams triumphantly. "The British know better than to risk a riot."

"Rotch is mighty anxious about his ship. He wants to save both the tea and the ship. He'll keep on going to Governor Hutchinson day after day, and ask him to send the tea back with the ships," said John Hancock smiling.

"And Hutchinson'll refuse," cried Adams, his eyes glowing. "By the time the twenty days are up, everybody in Boston will know we've asked that the ships and tea be sent back peaceably. On the very last day, we'll hold a public meeting at South Church."

"That will be the sixteenth of December," said Josiah Quincy in his deep ringing voice.

"Rotch will come to the meeting right from the governor. If Rotch tells us that the governor promised to send the ships back within a half an hour, I'll say—'Now may God help my country'— But if he tells us the governor refused his petition—" Samuel Adams spoke in a loud excited voice, his eyes glinted, his head bobbed, and his arm shook.

He doesn't really want that tea sent back, thought Robert, amazed at his discovery.

"What then?" asked John Adams, his pink face smiling.

"I will then say—'This meeting can do nothing more to save the country,'" exclaimed Samuel Adams in a jubilant voice. "That will be the signal for patriots to act," he added solemnly. His cousin, John Adams, looked a little bit abashed.

Everybody began to talk. "Young man," Samuel Adams turned to Robert, "raise your hand and swear by Almighty God that you will not let one word you heard here tonight pass your lips."

Robert felt terrified and glad at the same time. Everything was happening too fast. But it was better that way, he decided. It gave him no time to hesitate. He felt certain now that he wanted to belong to the Sons of Liberty, come what might. He raised his hand and said in a high shaky voice, "I swear by Almighty God."

The slovenly maid brought in some tankards of punch. They sat and talked and made plans. Robert's head was in a whirl. Where would he go now? he wondered. John Hancock rose to go at last, and looked at Robert. "You'll need a place to sleep the night," he said in his offhand manner. "I guess we can put you up at my house. Come along, young man."

There were three ships along Griffin's wharf now that the belated *Beaver* had arrived. Robert was too busy getting acquainted with his new friends and his job in Hancock's warehouse to notice how the days went by. The sixteenth of December arrived suddenly, it seemed to him. The bells of Boston had been ringing since early morning. Everybody was on the streets. Old South Church was crowded from wall to wall. Thousands of people were standing in the crowded sidewalks, unmindful of the cold wind and rain. Robert dressed himself as a Mohawk warrior and smeared his face with war paint. On his head was a headdress made of an old stocking stuck with feathers. Under his blanket, which he wore like an Indian robe, he had a stout hatchet in his belt. He was to stay close to the company of Mohawks. And above all, he was not to talk. None of them were to talk. Inside South Church, Samuel Adams and Josiah Quincy were taking turns talking to the crowd. Now and then Josiah Quincy quoted a passage from the Scriptures. The crowd waited patiently. Something was going to happen, some knew what it was, others did not. Suddenly there was a shout—"There's Mr. Rotch."

A young man worked his way through the crowd and dashed into the church. He was very pale and his lips trembled. He stumbled up the aisle and whispered with Josiah Quincy and Samuel Adams. Everyone stretched forward to see what was going on.

Samuel Adams tried to appear calm, but his palsied arm shook and his head bobbed. There was a sudden silence.

"This meeting can do nothing more to save the country," he announced in a loud shaking voice. There was a spot of red on his sallow cheeks.

Instantly an Indian war whoop went up, whistles began to blow, and everyone was shouting. In a few minutes the church was empty. Everyone was shouting and running, following a company of Mohawks smeared with war paint.

"Tea for the fishes," shouted someone. Young boys, their faces blacked with soot, took up the shout—"Tea for the fishes."

"Quiet," shouted a stocky man, dressed as an Indian chieftain wearing a feathered headdress. That was Paul Revere; Robert rec-

ognized his voice and his thickset body. And now there were only whispers as they ran through the dark streets, hugging their hatchets and axes under their blankets—Down Salt Lane, Sea Street, Flounder Alley. Robert knew the streets by heart. He kept to the front of the crowd to show the way to the younger men, dressed as he was, in Indian blankets, feathers and war paint. He had never felt so excited in his life. They reached the waterfront at last. The moon had come out, and it had stopped raining. The water shimmered calm and clear in the moonlight; the ships at anchor looked secure and peaceful. Robert felt glad now, as he stood there a moment, that no harm was to be done to the ships.

The wharf was crowded with thousands of people, but not a word was spoken. Suddenly a boatswain's whistle sounded loud and shrill. Paul Revere moved silently and swiftly through the crowd and divided the company into three groups. The captain of the *Dartmouth* appeared on the deck of his ship.

"Captain stay in cabin," the Indian chief addressed the captain persuasively. "Me take tea, me no hurt ship."

The captain listened to him a moment, grunted something, waved his hand as if to brush him aside, and went back to his cabin. A cabin boy appeared and handed the Indian chief the keys to the hatch and led him solemnly to the hold where the chests of tea were stored.

The *Eleanor* and the *Beaver* were now being warped in to the wharf. Indians were swarming the decks of all three ships. All one could hear presently was the groaning and the rattling of winches. Indians swarmed down into the holds. Large chests of tea came to sight. It seemed to Robert as if he were in a dream and that the next minute he would waken and see his uncle and Mr. Billings taking inventory. He followed his companions into the holds. The chests were heavy; hatchets and axes battered them open. Inside the chests, the tea was wrapped in thick canvas; knives glinted in the semidarkness, ripping the canvas apart. A delicious smell of fragrant tea filled the salty air.

"Into the sea every last crumb of tea," shouted the Indian chief as he noticed how Robert hesitated and sniffed at the tea; shaking his head, thinking again of his uncle.

Boxes were dragged close to the rail, the canvas wrappings were lifted in strong hands and tossed overboard. Tea floated on the water like a dark crust of foam—"A mighty tasty brew of tea," chuckled a secret voice from under a mask of paint.

A short distance away the two men of war, the *Active* and the *Kingfisher*, could be seen plainly in the moonlight. The British Marine might open fire and disperse the tea party. But Governor Hutchinson had not asked the British Marine to intervene. A riot was the last thing he wanted.

It was almost dawn by the time all the tea from the three ships was in the water. Someone let out a wild shout of delight.

Samuel Adams and John Hancock, standing at a respectable distance away from the ships, were watching what was going on, as if they didn't know what it was all about. Someone began to sing, another one to play a fife. The Indians found brooms somewhere, and were now sweeping the decks clean. The captain stole out of his cabin at last and watched them depart, a sneaking look of admiration in his eyes for their high spirit. "Who'll pay for it all?" he asked, seeing only Robert still wrapped in his blanket standing on deck.

But Robert had no answer, for he was asking himself that same question. Now that the excitement was over, he felt somewhat uneasy. What would happen, he wondered.

Samuel Adams and a few others were talking in low voices as they walked away from the wharf in the gray light of dawn. Robert hastened to catch up with them.

"An expensive tea party, a most expensive tea party," John Hancock was saying in his high jovial voice. "And if I am not mistaken, the British Parliament will make us pay for it."

"They will try," said Samuel Adams mysteriously.

"And shall we pay for it, sir?" asked Robert diffidently.

"We shall see," said Samuel Adams, an unrelenting glint in his eyes.

THOMAS JEFFERSON
—— 1776 ——

*"I have sworn upon the altar of God eternal hostility
against every form of tyranny over the mind of man."*

THE STREETS OF PHILADELPHIA WERE FULL OF
people: young men in new militia uniforms, ladies in silks and
laces, riding in sedan chairs, workmen in rough homespun, ped-
dlers, hawkers, and many strangers from the thirteen colonies. A
man with a wheelbarrow pushed his way through the crowds to

knock at one door after another. No one paid attention to him as they hurried on their way. But now and then, men stopped at street corners to talk, and to ask the question that was on their minds—*What would King George do if the colonies declared for independence?* The Continental Congress was holding meetings at the State House. No one knew what would come out of these deliberations.

Mrs. Graff was polishing her candlesticks when the man with the wheelbarrow stopped to knock at the door of her new brick house. Who could it be, knocking so loud, she wondered.

"Have you anything made of lead?" the man asked when she came to the door.

"I have none for sale, if that's what you want," said Mrs. Graff. She was about to shut the door when the man put his foot in the doorway.

"I've not come to buy or to sell," he said. "It's to be donated."

"Donated?" Mrs. Graff looked indignant. She was a newly married housekeeper, proud of her spick and span brick house and her precious possessions.

"To make bullets," explained the man, displaying a badge under his coat. On it was printed in black letters—"Sons of Liberty."

Mrs. Graff looked at the badge, and from the badge to the wheelbarrow piled high with all kinds of utensils. "Bullets?" she repeated in a dazed voice. She wanted to cry, but it was no use. She knew that if she refused to give him anything, he might report that she was for King George and therefore a Tory. Unpleasant things happened to Tories these days; some were even known to have been tarred and feathered. She went to the cupboard and brought out her polished candlesticks. The man threw them into the wheelbarrow, and trudged away to knock on other doors.

"Bullets," muttered Mrs. Graff; all kinds of fearful thoughts came into her head. She went out to sit on the white stone step to watch for her lodger. She would ask him about it. He would know, she reasoned. He had come all the way from Virginia to sit in the Continental Congress with the delegates from the thirteen colonies. But Thomas Jefferson had left his apartment early to walk in the cool of the morning and prepare his thoughts for the debates.

A short man with a sallow face overtook Thomas Jefferson as he neared the State House. "To my mind," said the man by way of greeting, "there's no need for further debate."

"I am of the same opinion," said Jefferson with a quiet smile.

"Richard Henry Lee stated it clearly in his proposed resolution: that the Congress should declare that these United Colonies are, and of a right ought to be, free and independent states. Why do we wait to make our declaration?" demanded Samuel Adams in a peppery voice. "In Massachusetts we're ready for the revolution. We've proven it at Bunker Hill." He pronounced the word "revolution" in a ringing voice as if he liked the sound of the word. In his mind it stood for a brave free world.

Jefferson smiled. He chose his words with great care. The word "revolution" was not mentioned at the meetings at the State House. They called the king a tyrant, they spoke of misrule by the English Parliament and talked of independence and of liberty. Only at the tavern over their dinner was the word "revolution" mentioned.

"What are we waiting for?" Samuel Adams repeated the question as Jefferson remained thoughtfully silent. "Are we waiting for King George to hang us, before we make up our minds?"

"In Virginia they think the declaration's been made," said Jefferson at last. "But there are those colonies who are only half convinced, as you know. We wait for them. We must be of one mind about so great a matter."

They had come to the State House now. The delegates were arriving, greeting each other with sober faces, each one thinking his own thoughts.

It was a warm June day. From the nearby stables came the smell of horses and the buzz of flies. The debate started where it left off the day before—"If it comes to war, we may be caught and hanged as rebels and then the condition in the colonies will be worse than it is now," argued one of the delegates.

John Adams stood up and began to speak. Jefferson listened in silence. He was not as eloquent a talker as John Adams. He could write his thoughts much more clearly than any of them; but just now John Adams was saying what he would say if he were to stand up and talk.

"Richard Henry Lee of Virginia has stated it clearly for us all in his proposed resolution," called out one delegate from a side seat.

"Let the resolution be read," called out another voice.

The secretary, Charles Thomson, read the resolution in a clear loud voice ". . . Resolved that these United Colonies are and of a right ought to be free and independent states . . ."

A solemn silence followed, and then suddenly president John Hancock called for a vote. The resolution was passed, with loud ayes, but there were a few ayes that sounded a little faint; the delegates looked at each other half fearful, half triumphant.

The die was cast. The Declaration of Independence must now be written out and presented to the people.

Mrs. Graff went about with a long face. She missed her candlesticks. But that was not all she had on her mind. If war came, the redcoats, she reasoned, were sure to win. There were plenty of them in the colonies and more in England. They were trained soldiers; they had arms and ammunition. Her husband was a bricklayer and her brothers were farmers. If it came to war, what would they know about shooting and killing? When Henry, her young nephew, brought her eggs from his father's farm late one afternoon, she began to tell him about her candlesticks, and about the Sons of Liberty.

But Henry was much more interested in asking her questions about her lodger—"Is it true that Thomas Jefferson's name is written on the king's list of outlaws in England?" he asked her.

Mrs. Graff looked more alarmed than ever. "Who told you that?"

"Reginald said so. Reginald heard his father tell a man that Mr. Jefferson would be the first one hanged for a rebel. His name was on the King's list for a long time now because he wrote a paper. 'Summary Views from Virginia' it was called, he said. It made King George angry, and he called Jefferson a dangerous rebel. Reginald said Jefferson is a wicked man. He owns lots of slaves and he beats them with whips."

"Reginald's father is a Tory, that's the reason he talks like that," frowned Mrs. Graff. "You'd better keep away from Reginald, or you'll get into trouble."

"What if he is a Tory? He lets me ride his horse and hunt with him. I don't care who is a Tory and who isn't," said Henry.

Bob, Jefferson's slave, came into the kitchen now. He filled a large pitcher with water to have it ready for his master when he came back from the State House. Henry followed the young Negro up the stairs to the two-room apartment, a sitting room on one side of the stairs, a bedroom on the other side.

"Is it true Mr. Jefferson beats his slaves with a leather whip?" asked Henry, standing in the doorway.

"No sir, never nobody ever been beat in Monticello." Bob looked amazed at the question. "No, sir," he repeated, "Massa be gen'le, he be kind—"

"How many slaves has he?" asked Henry, watching Bob smooth the bed, and arrange towels on the washstand.

Bob showed glistening white teeth in a proud smile. "We has thousan' and mebby two thousan'. We has a big house on top o' mountain. It sure is cool up there, we has big trees, and we has flowers, and we has birds a singin'. Monticello we calls the place," Bob wagged his head in pride. "An' we has ho'ses, fines' ho'ses in the whole wo'ld, we has."

"I heard say that your master came on horseback all the way from Virginia, but I don't believe it," said Henry.

"Massa shure did come ridin' his ho'se all the way, he shure did," smiled Bob. "We has the ho'se in the stable waitin' to bring massa home. An' me, I'm waitin' too," he added with another smile.

Henry looked around the small sitting room with its plain furniture, and wondered what made Jefferson want to leave his fine house and come to this place, and get mixed up with rebels, and be hanged maybe, when he could be up there on his mountain with slaves and horses and all kinds of fine things.—"What's in that box?" he asked, trying to open what looked like a wooden box on the table.

A firm footfall could now be heard on the stairs. The next instant a tall slender gentleman entered the sitting room. Henry took his hand off the box, and looked down on the floor, his face red.

"I am pleased to find a visitor," said Thomas Jefferson in a friendly voice. "I see that you are interested in that box," he added with a slow smile.

"I thought maybe there might be pistols in there," stammered Henry.

"It holds something more deadly than pistols," said Jefferson with a shake of the head.

"More deadly than pistols?" Henry repeated the words, greatly puzzled.

Jefferson took a small key from his pocket and unlocked the box.

"It's a desk," exclaimed Henry, much amazed. "I never saw a desk like that."

"That's because there isn't another one like it—I designed it, and had it made," explained Jefferson. "Very convenient; can be used on horseback if necessary." He sat down in a chair, the desk unfolded on his lap to show Henry how he used it.

Henry stared at the sheets of paper covered with fine writing. "But that's only paper," he said at last, no longer frightened.

Jefferson sorted the papers in silence for a while. "Only papers?" he stacked the shining white sheets carefully one on top of the other—"What's written on these pages is our ammunition. It is ideas we really fight with, and when an idea is true and right, it is more powerful than swords and pistols. If you understand this, you'll fight on the right side always."

Henry felt almost awed as he stood there, looking at Jefferson's pale face so kind and genial. He did not understand exactly what it was he was saying, but he knew, somehow, that what he said was wise and true, and that he was a great man.

"Thank you, sir," he said, backing out of the room. Never again would he believe what Reginald said about Thomas Jefferson. He came down the stairs two steps at a time. Let Reginald be a Tory; he, Henry, would be on Jefferson's side from now on.

"You shouldn't be going upstairs to Mr. Jefferson's rooms, he doesn't want to be disturbed," scolded Mrs. Graff.

"I'm going to join the Sons of Liberty as soon as I'm old enough," said Henry by way of an answer.

Mrs. Graff shook her head and sighed. Her husband told her in secret, that he had heard Mr. Jefferson was writing a declaration of rights up there in their sitting room. Mr. Jefferson was a very fine gentleman, anyone could see that. He gave her no trouble; but she was not at all sure that it was quite safe to have him in their house. No one knew which way the tide might turn. And now her young nephew was talking about wanting to join the Sons of Liberty. What had Jefferson said to Henry to make him turn about like that? she wondered uneasily. "You'll be sleeping on the third floor right over his sitting room while you are visiting us; don't you go disturbing him," she warned.

Thomas Jefferson was also thinking about Henry as he settled down to work at his small desk on his lap. The boy was an upstanding, promising young person. He and many others like him might have to take a gun in their hands before long to back up what he was writing here on these sheets of foolscap. He rose to pace the floor, his face clouded now. Ever since the beginning of time, blind and selfish men had forced brave men to fight for freedom and justice. Each time the choice had to be made anew. The vision came when the need was greatest and the hearts of men were willing; and always, there were enough brave men to carry the banner of progress, and to fight for it.

His quill moved slowly over the white paper, writing and rewriting. What he was writing here must proclaim their cause, make it clear to themselves and to the world— ". . . When in the course of human events, it becomes necessary for one people to dissolve the political bands which have connected them with another, and to assume, among the powers of the earth, the separate and equal station to which the laws of nature and of nature's God entitle them . . ."

The house was steeped in stillness. The scratching of the quill on the paper sounded like a voice. He was meeting the future: a great nation mighty in youth and freedom. He must not say too much nor too little. He wished for a moment that both Benjamin Franklin and John Adams, who were appointed to write this declaration with him, were present now. But the aged Benjamin Franklin, busy on many other committees, delegated the task to the two younger men, and John Adams declared that he had argued so much for independence, his name must have become odious to the people, and insisted that Jefferson was the proper man to compose this paper for he had greater felicity of expression.

Jefferson had accepted this task with fear and trembling; the purpose of this declaration was too sacred to make it less than great. Again he paced the floor, weighing each phrase and word. Franklin and Adams had approved his first draft; he must choose words with no doubtful meanings. Each word must be a sword to pierce the thickness of the flesh.

It was warm in the room. He opened the window and the door to make a draught. The candles sputtered in the feeble breeze. He held the pen suspended above the paper and read aloud what he had written—". . . We hold these truths to be self-evident—that all men are created equal; that they are endowed by their Creator with certain unalienable rights; that among these are life, liberty and the pursuit of happiness . . ."

In the room above, Henry lay awake on the narrow bed. It was too warm to sleep, but that was not the only reason he was awake. His thoughts circled round and round; something strange had happened to him. He did not know what it was and it frightened him a little. Through the open door he could hear the scratching of the pen on the paper and the low voice reading something he did not altogether understand. But the words excited him. They made him feel brave. He wished with all his might to be a man. But no matter, he would certainly fight on Mr. Jefferson's side as soon as he was old enough, he promised himself as he fell asleep at last.

Henry's father had a small farm not far from the city. He was neither for the Tories, nor against them. He sold milk and eggs to his neighbors and he didn't care whether they were Tories or not.

When Henry came home from his visit, and began to tell his father about Thomas Jefferson, and what he said to him, Henry's father told him to mind his own business, and chop wood for kin-

THAT ALL MEN
EQUAL, THAT
ENDOWED
CREATOR
UNALIENA

dling. Henry chopped wood, but his thoughts went back to the papers in the small desk Mr. Jefferson showed him. He remembered every word Jefferson said to him, and how he looked. It was hard not to talk about it, and he was glad when Reginald came sauntering by on his sleek horse and stopped to talk to him.

"We might go hunting next week maybe," offered Reginald.

"I've got something better to do," said Henry.

"Better than hunting?" Reginald looked very surprised. "There isn't anything better than hunting."

"Yes, there is," said Henry. "But you wouldn't know," he added with a mysterious air.

"What are you talking about?" cried Reginald, much annoyed.

"You wouldn't understand because you're a Tory," said Henry.

"I certainly am a Tory. We're subject to the Crown of England, aren't we?" demanded Reginald.

"I'm for freedom, like Mr. Jefferson," said Henry proudly.

"You mean you're for the rebels?" Reginald got off his horse in his excitement. "You're crazy, you'll be hanged by the neck with all the other traitors as soon as they're caught."

"Then I'll be in good company—better company than the Tories," said Henry doggedly.

"You traitor!" shouted Reginald, red in the face with anger.

"You old Tory!" shouted Henry. "I'm going to join the Sons of Liberty and help tar and feather all the Tories we find."

"You will, will you?" Reginald struck Henry in the face. The next minute they were pounding each other with their fists. Reginald's fists were not as tough as Henry's. He was getting the worst of it.

"I'll have my father put you in jail," he cried, trying to stop his nosebleed with his fine white cambric handkerchief.

"You better tell your father to hide under the bed before the Sons of Liberty smear him with tar and stick feathers all over him, and you too," cried Henry.

"You'll be flogged and put in jail," threatened Reginald as he rode away.

But when Reginald told his father about Henry, his father remained silent, his face pale with apprehension. Half his help at his elegant store on Chestnut Street, he suspected, were rebels, and were secretly wearing badges of Sons of Liberty. No one knew these days what might happen to anyone.

At the State House, the Continental Congress was discussing the now completed Declaration of Independence. Jefferson listened in silence: let them pick and argue, let them tear it apart, he had spoken for the people. It was their voice as well as his. He knew their mind, he had listened to their complaints and to their hopes. They were of a mind to be a free, independent country. What would they do with this freedom? Would they know, all of them together, how to shape this new nation into a great nation?

Franklin, sitting near by, watched the younger man with a smile of sympathy. Was he perhaps troubled by the arguments over his composition? He came over to sit beside Jefferson.

"I'll tell you a story," he offered with a droll smile. "A man I knew opened a hat store, and hung a sign over the door. It had a picture of a hat and read 'John Thompson, hatter, makes and sells hats for ready money.' When he asked his customers for their opinion of his sign, one said the word 'hatter' should be omitted because the words 'makes hats' told he was a hatter; another customer said the word 'makes' should be left out because customers wouldn't care who made the hats; another one said the words 'for ready money' should be left out as everyone who bought a hat expected to pay. The sign now read 'John Thompson sells hats.' Why have 'sells hats' on the sign? asked a friend. Nobody will expect you to give them away, and why have the word 'hats' when there is a picture of a hat on the sign? So now all there was left was the picture of a hat and the name John Thompson."

Jefferson listened with an amused smile. Franklin was telling him this story, he realized, not only to take his mind off the debate over his composition but to make him see that the important things in the declaration would remain. That was, after all, what mattered. Let them argue about this word or that word; the Declaration of men's rights was now complete, and it was to be proclaimed to the world.

The weighing of words ended at last. Solemnly, and in a loud voice, John Hancock called for a vote. The room rang with aye, aye, but not all the ayes were loud and glad, some were low and timid.

The Declaration of Independence was adopted.

"We may hang for this," muttered a few low voices.

"Aye, we may hang for this, but if we don't hang together we shall certainly hang separately," said Franklin. He was fond of repeating this pleasantry.

John Hancock laughed louder than any of them. The British Parliament interfered with his importing and exporting; now he would be free of their interference at last. But there was no time to waste on more talk. The Declaration must be printed as quickly as possible. John Hancock gave the order to send it to the printer immediately. Special messengers on horseback were to carry printed copies to every city, town and hamlet to be read aloud in public. The printer worked all night to have enough copies ready for all the commanders in the army to read to troops in every courthouse in the colonies.

Jefferson was now free to go home to his beloved Monticello. He went shopping in the handsome stores on Chestnut Street he much admired. He bought presents, and paid the bill for the seven pairs of gloves he had bought for his wife. He paid for a thermometer he had bought when he first arrived. He felt gay and buoyant. He bought a ticket for two shillings, to see some monkeys on exhibition.

Bob, his young slave, packed his bags and waited patiently to leave the hot and noisy city. But Jefferson remained to listen to the public reading of the Declaration in the yard of the State House.

An eager crowd was waiting to hear the reading. The young Navy officer looked around at the expectant faces, his eyes solemn and serious. His voice rang out clear and strong in the solemn silence ". . . We hold these truths to be self-evident, that all men are created equal, that they are endowed by their Creator with certain unalienable rights, that among these are life, liberty and the pursuit of happiness . . ."

A loud shout went out from the crowd when the reading ended. Singing riotous songs, the crowd broke into the State House, dragged the king's coat of arms from the hall, and set fire to it in the square. Everybody was shouting and singing—bonfires were lighted, guns saluted, bells rang—

Standing somewhat apart, Jefferson watched the crowd, his serious eyes alight with a strange smile. Young Henry spied him in the crowd, and came up to stand beside him. The ringing of the great bell on the steeple of the State House swelled the din of the many-throated voice of the people. One could hardly make out what anyone said. A man with a white beard, standing near by, edged his way towards Jefferson and called out—"Did you know, sir, the words that are molded on the top of the bell?" and without waiting for Jefferson to answer he added, "It's a verse from the Bible. It's been there since 1751 and it says 'Proclaim Liberty throughout all the land unto all the Inhabitants thereof'— It's a prophecy, sir, I guess."

"And so it is," exclaimed Jefferson.

Henry looked up at the bell in wonder. "To think it has all been written there and we didn't know it," he said in a voice of awe.

"Some of us knew it," smiled the old man as he edged away through the crowd. Henry moved nearer to Jefferson and displayed his badge of the Sons of Liberty he was wearing on his chest. "I'm going to fight, sir, as soon as they'll let me," he said proudly. "I'm going to be in the militia."

Jefferson shook the boy's hand and walked back to his rooms for final preparations to go home. But he did not sleep that night. Bells rang all through the night and people sang around bonfires until their voices grew hoarse. Jefferson went out to walk in the streets. He was going home, his farm needed looking after—things were in a muddle there after so long an absence, but his thoughts were not on his own affairs this night.

He listened to the songs and the tolling of bells and feet dancing on sidewalks. This was the lusty voice of a new nation, the United States of America: a democracy shouting its freedom. He wanted to savor it, taste it, and remember this to the end of his days.

GEORGE WASHINGTON

— 1776 —

"Let us raise a standard to which the wise and honest can repair; the event is in the hands of God."

TWO SENTRIES, IN TATTERED UNIFORMS, WERE TALKing in low voices in the entry of the fieldstone farmhouse.

"I guess he knows we're beaten," the younger of the two men nodded towards the large room where George Washington was walking up and down, his head bent low on his chest.

"You're wrong, Bill," exclaimed the older man. " 'Don't talk of yesterday, tomorrow is more pertinent.' That's what he said to us after Germantown. He'll find a way—"

"You're a bookish man, Nat, you can talk. I'm practical. Facts is facts. We've been beaten all the way from New York across Westchester and up across New Jersey. And we didn't believe we were licked." Bill stooped down to wrap the rags around his bare feet. "We thought we'd sure trap the redcoats at Germantown." He jerked the rag up around his ankles with an angry frown. "They licked us again. We lost half our men at Germantown."

At this moment, the outside door was pulled open. A sharp gust of wind freshened the stale air for a moment. Young Hamilton entered hurriedly and banged the door shut. He had no overcoat, and his nose was blue with cold. He glanced at the sentry, received their salute with a haughty gesture, and went into the large, low-ceilinged room to whisper with Washington.

"I guess something's up," Nat leaned over to mumble to Bill. "I feel it in my bones."

"All I can feel is the wind down my back." Bill shivered and wriggled his frostbitten fingers to take the numbness out.

The outside door opened again. General Greene entered, letting in another draft of wind. The sentry stood at attention and saluted. General Greene, a tall handsome man, his uniform stained with blood and smears of mud, returned the salute with a preoccupied air, walked swiftly into the large room, and laid a penciled chart on the table.

Washington leaned forward to examine the chart, and Hamilton unrolled a map, and laid it beside the chart. The word "attack" spoken in a low voice, reached Nat in the entry. Nat glanced anxiously at Bill to see if he had heard. But Bill, busy with his thoughts, was paying no attention.

"The morale of the men is poor; in fact, it is very bad," said General Greene in a low voice. "I'm afraid there'll be many deserters when the men find out we're planning to attack Trenton on Christmas Day."

"A few good floggings would put an end to deserting," said young Hamilton smartly.

"I hope it won't come to that." Washington sighed and went over to the window to look out at the bleak New Jersey hills, coated in snow. If only Congress would remember that his men needed boots, and that an army had to eat, he was thinking sadly.

Nat tried to catch a hint of what the officers were talking about in the large room, but their voices were so low he could only guess at a word now and then. He felt sure they were planning something important. He looked at Bill's red unhappy face and shook his head sadly—Bill was very young.

"The generals told us we'd be celebrating Christmas in Philadelphia," said Bill, half to himself half to Nat. "But Congress is smart; they know the redcoats'll take Philadelphia and they got themselves off to Baltimore. They're safe, and we're cooped up here in this valley, eating frozen potatoes, and glad to get even that," Bill spat onto the dusty floor.

"The redcoats haven't got Philadelphia yet," said Nat and began to whistle "Yankee Doodle."

General Washington turned from the window and glanced through the half-open door at his sentry. A shadow of a smile flickered into his tired eyes. "There's spirit in our men yet," he said softly. "But only a quick victory now can save our revolution."

General Greene studied the map as if he didn't know it by heart. "A surprise attack is our chief hope for success," he said thoughtfully.

"Some of the generals are of the opinion that we would have a better chance in the spring. We'd have more men," broke in Hamilton.

"By spring it would be all over with us," Washington spoke little above a whisper, but there was a determined ring in his voice and a flare of fire in his gray eyes. "We attack Trenton on the night of Christmas Day." He leaned over the table and began to explain his plan: "Putnam and his men will come up from Philadelphia. Ewing and his men will cross near Trenton and join us before we cross the river. Glover's Marblehead fishermen will man the boats."

General Greene pulled a small much-handled pamphlet from his pocket and began to read aloud—"These are times that try a man's soul . . ."

" 'Try a man's soul,' yes!" said Washington taking the pamphlet to page it in silence for a while. "Our men should read this pamphlet," he said, handing it back to General Greene. "We need what Thomas Paine has written here," Washington spoke slowly and with deliberation. He no longer looked harassed and tired. "I see that Paine calls this pamphlet the *Crisis*. His pamphlet, *Common Sense,* worked a powerful change in the minds of many men at the time when we were not certain of the revolution. This is the worst crisis we've ever had since then."

"Yes, Howe thinks we're finished, and Cornwallis is sending his baggage to New York to ship to England," said General Greene.

"Colonel Rahl and his Hessians are making great preparations for Christmas. They're boasting that we're done and finished for good. All the Tories in Trenton are planning parties for them." Hamilton said this with a smile, as if he were telling a joke.

"They'll discover they are mistaken," said Washington walking up and down, a frown on his face. He stopped in the center of the room, the frown on his face deepened. "Our victory depends on a surprise attack, take every precaution, gentlemen."

A sergeant appeared suddenly and stood saluting.

"What are you doing here?" demanded Washington in quick anger.

"Making beds, sir," said the sergeant. "Do you wish for water, sir?"

"We wish for nothing," Washington made a gesture for him to go out through the entry.

The sergeant saluted and hurried out past the sentry without looking at them.

"Walls have ears," said Hamilton, mysteriously. "They say there is a spy, but no one is certain."

"Keep an eye on the man," Washington frowned darkly.

The sergeant was in the kitchen whispering with the cook when Hamilton found him at last.

"There's to be punch for the officers on Christmas Eve," grinned the sergeant with an innocent air.

Hamilton was not at all convinced that the sergeant and the cook were talking about punch. And yet they might have been, mused Hamilton. There was a large punch bowl standing on the table. Where did the cook get it, and what had they to make punch with? he wondered as he went to report his suspicions to Washington.

Christmas Eve came around in a storm of snow and sleet. The men in the encampment were not celebrating Christmas Eve. A rumor was being circulated in deep secret. They were to attack the Hessians at Trenton. At supper, an officer had announced that deserters would be caught and flogged without quarter. Bill and Nat, not on duty this evening, relaxed in the light of the wood fire.

"At home now," Bill said half aloud, "they're singing carols maybe. There's a tree with presents and there's fruitcake and there's a yule log in the fireplace, and wreaths in the windows and mistletoe—" Bill fell silent, thinking of his folks at home, and of Nellie his sweetheart, smiling from behind the window curtains, waiting for him to come home. He looked around the dreary barracks, half dugout, half built of rough hewn logs. He had had enough of this war, he thought to himself. Flogging or no flogging, he was going to get away from here before the night was over. His mind was made up. He had it all planned.

The men were whispering, telling each other what they had heard, trying to figure it out—

"Something's up all right. General Washington's been talking to the officers in secret—"

"Ay, and the sergeants are taking inventory of ammunition and ordered to have guns and bayonets cleaned and ready—"

"Maybe it's just to keep us occupied—" speculated Nat.

Bill listened to the talk, but it didn't matter to him, he told himself. He was clearing out this very night. He unwrapped the rags around his feet, and tried to warm his frostbitten toes with the palms of his hands. A pair of officer's boots he had found in the rubbish heap were tucked away under the straw sack that served for a bed. The boots had no soles, but they would keep his rags from slipping off his feet when he walked through the deep snow. He knew of a Quaker a few miles away. The Quaker, reasoned Bill, did not believe in war. If he could manage to get to that Quaker's farm, he would be safe. The Quaker would certainly let him remain hidden in the hay, if he found him in his barn on Christmas Day. Bill felt in his pocket. He had managed to hide one of the wretched potatoes to take with him. It would keep him from starving in case he had to stay in hiding longer than he hoped.

An officer entered the dugout suddenly. He had a solemn expression on his weatherbeaten face. He did not say, "Merry Christmas," but he said in a calm clear voice, "This is Christmas Eve, my men." He sat down on a pile of fire wood, and looked around him at the uneasy faces, and said, after a moment's silence, "You all know Thomas Paine, aide de camp to General Greene—a good man. Didn't mind what he turned his hand to, nursed and cooked on occasion." The officer talked in a friendly voice.

"Ay, we know Tom Paine," called out several voices.

"Tom Paine wrote a pamphlet, he called it the *Crisis* because we're in a crisis," went on the officer. "It's full of gunpowder; it's like a cannon fired inside of you." The officer looked around at the inquiring puzzled faces staring at him. "Well, we need it," he said quietly. He opened the pamphlet he was holding in his hand, and began to read aloud:

"'These are the times that try men's souls . . . The summer soldier and the sunshine patriot will, in this crisis, shrink from the service of their country . . . he that stands it now deserves the love and thanks of men and women . . .'" The officer glanced up for a moment and went on reading. "'Tyranny, like hell, is not easily conquered; yet we have this consolation with us, that the harder the conflict, the more glorious the triumph.'" The officer's voice rang out in the twilight with challenge. "'. . . Freedom should be highly rated . . . I call not upon a few but upon all in every state . . .'"

Bill sat with his shoulders hunched, his face turned away. He tried not to listen to the reading, but it seemed to him that every word rang out in the stillness like thunder.

The officer cleared his throat and went on reading, "'. . . I love a man that can smile in trouble, that can gather strength from distress and grow brave by reflection . . .'"

"That's the way Washington is," Nat nudged Bill. Bill moved uneasily. His face felt hot. There was sweat on his forehead, but his spine felt cold. It seemed to him that every word the officer read was addressed to him. If only he would stop reading that thing! But the officer kept it up. " '. . . I thank God I fear not. I see no real cause for fear . . . I can see the way out of it . . .' " The reading stopped suddenly. The officer looked around cautiously at the men.

"Read more," called out several voices. Bill shifted from side to side. All he wanted was to get away.

" 'We are fighting to make a new world, not for ourselves only but for all those yet unborn . . .' " The officer read on and stopped.

"Tom Paine marched with us from Germantown," whispered one of the men, nudging his companion.

"Ay," grunted the other, "we were beaten, and Tom Paine says to us—'Men live by glory,' he says— 'Our cause is just,' he says."

The officer listened to them in silence for a while. "Yes, Tom Paine said many things we need to think about now—good night, men, rest well," the officer left them as abruptly as he had come.

"I saw Tom Paine write that pamphlet." Nat edged closer to Bill. "He wrote it on top of a drum he held between his knees. He was a man to stir you to the heart," ruminated Nat. "He made you understand." Bill remained motionless, his head on his knees. He did not want to look at Nat.

Nat fell silent at last, thinking of General Washington—The General looked tired these days; he hardly took time to rest, pacing the floor, thinking, thinking, thinking. If it were true that he had decided to attack Trenton, he must have a good reason.

"Washington is a brave general, he is also a wise general, I am with him on everything he decides to do," Nat turned to Bill again. "Washington is not thinking of his own safety. He is thinking only of the revolution, and that is all that counts." But Bill, sitting there his head on his knees, did not seem to hear him.

Some of them would not come back, thought Nat. Perhaps it would be he. Nat's thoughts switched to his wife and to his small son, waiting for him at home. He remembered the day he left for the army; and now suddenly he understood more clearly that grand

and proud feeling he had that day, and what Washington meant when he made his brief remarks, and what Jefferson meant when he wrote the Declaration of Independence. They were fighting for something larger than all of them put together. They were fighting for Liberty. They would win. Washington didn't doubt, neither would he. Yes, they would win, they must. He went to sleep thinking of that.

Bill lay awake listening to the men talking. They were sure now that there was to be an attack on Trenton. They talked and speculated and went off to sleep at last. Bill felt his heart pounding against his ribs. It seemed to him that everyone must hear it, it sounded so loud. He leaned on his elbow thinking and planning. In the corner of the hut, there was a hole under the rubble, large enough for a man to crawl out, if he lay flat on his stomach. Bill stared at the dying embers in the ashes. He tried not to think of anything but the way to get to that hole without waking anyone. But instead, thoughts about George Washington swarmed in his head. In the darkness, he saw his face as if he were there: pale and very tired. Bill tried to push this image out of his mind. But he couldn't; and he remembered, now, the kind look in his eyes when he looked at them and cheered them when everything seemed lost. "Don't think of yesterday, tomorrow is more pertinent"— that was the way he talked. He never gave up—"Men live by glory"—who said that? wondered Bill, and remembered it was Tom Paine said it. He had heard Tom Paine say it. What the officer had been reading to them came back to him now with a terrible impact. If he ran away, he would be a deserter. A shameful feeling came to Bill—and suddenly, he knew that he could not be a deserter. No matter what happened, he would remain and face it. He would take part and do his share. He lay back on his bunk, and closed his eyes. He was not frightened any more, nor hating war. A wonderful relief and gladness came to him now. He curled up, pulled the tattered covers around him and went to sleep.

At Trenton, the Tories were celebrating Christmas on a grand scale. The war was practically over, they told each other. By spring, the rebel army will run home to their plowing, their stores and offices, and whatever they had been doing before they took it into their foolish heads that they wanted Liberty.

Colonel Rahl, and his twelve hundred Hessians, received many invitations to dinners and to parties. At the large house, where Colonel Rahl was encamped with his staff of officers and orderlies, there were many guests on Christmas Day. There was singing and dancing, and a great dinner with much wine. They drank toasts to victory and told jokes about the American Army—

"The American Army, where is it?" Lieutenant Piel laughed. "The war is all over. Easter we go home to Germany." The lady he was dancing with understood only a few words of German. She laughed because she thought he was telling a funny story. "It is true," the Lieutenant said earnestly. "What is left of the American Army is hiding in holes, naked from the waist down," he let out a loud laugh, and the lady laughed with him because now she felt certain he was telling a funny story.

Colonel Rahl tried to dance too, but he did not feel very steady on his feet after drinking so many toasts to victory. He stepped on his partner's toes, and begged to be excused. He spoke only a few words in English and the lady spoke only a few words in German. A buzz of many voices filled the house; everybody was talking and singing German songs. The colonel liked the song. He clapped his hands and invited the ladies to sing with him.

"It will be spring soon; we will go home," cried a lieutenant.

"Yes, spring is beautiful in Germany," Major Von Dechow joined the conversation.

"Flowers, roses, oh roses," muttered Colonel Rahl.

It was hot in the room, though the windows rattled with the wind and the patter of sleet on the panes. Captain Altenbochen was the only one not too drunk to feel uneasy. He had something on his mind; he wanted to think it out. The room was full of tobacco smoke and there was too much noise with everybody singing, talking and laughing so loud. But some of the guests were going home at last. He was glad; he went out to get a breath of air. A sharp wind and a shower of sleet beat against his face. He walked down the path a little way, and peered into the inky darkness. If the Americans, he thought to himself, if they found out there was no patrol—what then, eh? he asked himself in the darkness. What if a spy reported to the Americans that their camp was unfortified? Colonel Rahl had called in the patrol to celebrate Christmas; a risky thing, thought the captain, wagging his head sadly. He looked around him uneasily and walked around to the back of the house. A man appeared from out the darkness, all wrapped up in a greatcoat and many scarfs. "Who goes?" challenged the captain in German. The man stood still and saluted. "I must see the Colonel," he said in English.

"Credentials," barked the captain, peering into the man's face, and recognizing one of the Tories, he heaved a sigh of relief. The man fished in his pocket and handed the captain a crumpled piece of paper. Another invitation, thought the captain. "Dankashun," he said in German, dismissing the man with a wave of the hand. The man bowed and trudged away in the darkness.

Captain Altenbochen returned to the house and leaned over the colonel now playing chess with Lieutenant Kiemm who did not know how to play chess and tried to bluff. But the colonel didn't mind; he couldn't quite remember whose move it was. "If the Americans find out we have no patrol tonight? If they attack?— The camp is unfortified," Captain Altenbochen blurted out.

"Dunner and Blitzen," roared the colonel. "The Americans are fools, but they aren't such fools. Not even a dog would go out on a night like this."

"May be, may be," mumbled the captain foolishly, and handed the colonel the note. The colonel unfolded the scrap of paper, and tried to read what was written there—If only those Tories could realize that he didn't know how to read English, he muttered, annoyed. He looked around him now for someone to translate the note to him. His American and English guests had gone home— Well, it didn't matter, just another invitation no doubt, or a request for a favor; he knew those Tories. They were never satisfied! He sighed. He felt very sleepy. He tucked the note into his pocket and climbed the stairs to his room. The bed was neat and waiting. He

tumbled into it half undressed, the note safe in his pocket. On it was written in English—"The Americans are going to attack tonight."

At this very moment, Washington and his men were marching down to the Delaware River. The wind, loaded with sleet, whipped their faces and blinded them. Their feet left bloody footmarks in the snow. But no one seemed to be aware of the cold and snow. Only one thought occupied them now—This time, they must win a victory. At the ferry crossing, Washington discovered that neither Putnam, Ewing, nor Caldwater had come. The storm was evidently too much for them. Washington looked at his men, taking their measure in one swift glance. He must make the attack alone with these twenty-four hundred men, and Glover's Marblehead fishermen to man the boats.

There was pity and pride in Washington's eyes as he watched the Marblehead boys take charge. They were used to storms at sea and to ice. Not one of them flinched. They faced the wind and sleet, expert and steadfast. Bill paused for one brief instant as he marched past Washington to take his place. Their eyes met, and in the hushed stillness, it seemed to Bill as if Washington spoke and said—"It is better to die for a great cause than to live for little things." He would remember this moment all his life, Bill thought to himself as the boats, tossed by wind and contrary current, plowed their way through sheets of floating ice.

The crossing took longer than Washington expected. It was four o'clock in the morning by the time the last boat touched the Trenton shore. And now there were six miles to march to the village street where the Hessians were encamped. They walked in silence, knee deep in the snow. It was slow marching. All was still, not a dog was in sight to bark a warning to the sleeping village. Every house, covered by a coat of snow, was shrouded in darkness. Washington separated his men into two divisions: one under Greene marched up inland; Sullivan marched his division along the river bank.

Bill marched beside Nat; he wanted to talk to him. Nat looked very calm and sure of himself. Bill swallowed hard; there was a strange feeling inside of him and he wanted to shout and to sing. He craned his neck to look towards Washington. How straight and tall he was, and his face stern as if he were made of stone. But there was a glint of fire in those gray eyes now. Bill felt very humble. He had a great desire to do something to prove that he was with him, not only in body but in spirit also. And at this moment each word Tom Paine wrote in the pamphlet the officer read to them the night before took on a new meaning.

A messenger from Sullivan ran up to Washington now. "The muskets are wet, sir. They can't be fired," he said in a hoarse whisper.

"Tell your general to use the bayonets, the town must be taken," snapped Washington in a commanding voice.

A gray line of light appeared on the horizon. The black night was coming to an end. They had not much farther to go now. The long village street stretched before them wide and straight. Sullivan's men charged up the road with their bayonets, shouting at the top of their lungs.

The houses came alive, doors and windows flew open, shouts and screams rang out in the gray dawn. Hessians, only half dressed, were pouring out into the street; bullets and bayonets greeted them from all sides. The bewildered Hessians, roused so suddenly from their drunken slumbers, swarmed and churned in circles, and tried to escape by the Brunswick Road. Sullivan's bayonets barred the way, and Washington sent rifle men to cut off escape.

Bill fought like mad. He hated to see blood gushing from wounds. He felt a little sick at the sight of so many Hessians lying in pools of blood in the snow. He saw Colonel Rahl rush out of the house shouting orders to his men. The colonel was hardly dressed, his jacket gaped open, his chest was bare. He was entirely sober now as he rushed back and forth trying to pull his men together to make a stand. Hessian soldiers brought out arms hastily. But Americans met them with bullets flying in all directions, from every side. Bayonets glimmered in the half-light, rifle shots rang out and pelted them like rain. Americans were shouting and singing. Hessian soldiers were lying in snow red with blood. Bill kept on firing. War was terrible, but this was no time to think or give in to feelings. He saw Rahl hit by a bullet. He saw him fall in the snow and lie still, blood running from his wound. A moment of terrible pity came to him. But it was all over now, he realized; the Hessians were laying down their arms.

"They are surrendering," shouted Nat.

Shouts of victory rang from every side.

Washington was saying something in a quiet voice. Bill could not make out what he said; but he could see Washington's face, no longer tired, nor stern, but strangely calm.

The Hessians stood unarmed now, their faces sullen.

"We must have got nearly a thousand Hessians," said Nat with pride, "and all their weapons and loot. Some of 'em escaped, about thirty killed, and some wounded," Nat felt shaky too. He wanted to talk to relieve his feelings. "We lost only two men and six wounded," he added, shaking Bill by the arm to rouse him from staring at the blood in the snow.

"War is terrible!" exclaimed Bill. His eyes felt hot.

"Our revolution is safe now," reminded Nat. "Those who thought we were finished will take heart now and come to our aid. That's what this battle means, Bill."

Washington, in a voice charged with compassion, was giving orders to care for the wounded. Bill began to help Nat carry groaning men into near-by houses. There will be more battles, Bill was thinking. But we'll win because our cause is just.

Nat was talking to him again in a low voice as if he wanted to make him share something he was seeing—"This is not for ourselves only." Nat was thinking of his small son at home—"It is for our children and for all those not yet born."

Washington turned to talk to General Greene now, making swift plans—"The Hessians shall parade through the streets in Philadelphia. Let the Tories see the revolution is not over. We'll send the Hessian flag to Baltimore to hang in the Hall of Congress. Men of good will will take heart."

"Men of good will will take heart," General Greene repeated thankfully. "They will come to our aid."

Washington looked around at his men in wordless gratitude. This victory was their victory. He wanted them to know it.

BENJAMIN FRANKLIN

—— *1778* ——

*"They that can give up essential liberty to obtain a
little temporary safety deserve neither liberty nor safety."*

THE *REPRISAL,* AN ARMED SLOOP, DRIVEN BY HIGH
winds, made slow progress over the lashing waves of the Atlantic.
Benjamin Franklin, and his two grandsons, spent much time on
deck, watching the spray dash against the sides of the ship. Every
day the stocky, slow-moving grandfather, absorbed in his own
meditations, took the temperature of the air and the water. His
seven-year-old namesake, Benjamin Franklin Bach, was greatly in-

terested in these rites. And even Temple, a young man of eighteen, was impressed when his grandfather dipped a net into the Gulf Stream and brought up a lively assortment of strange sea specimens.

The captain of the vessel, preoccupied with watching for suspicious-looking craft, paid small heed to these diversions. An English ship was an enemy, and doubly so on this voyage. If his ship were captured, Benjamin Franklin would be taken to London and hanged for a rebel. Temple and the small Ben speculated not a little on what might happen if their grandfather were taken prisoner. Would they be put in jail, or be hanged with him?

But Franklin only smiled when his small grandson questioned him about it. He was too deeply preoccupied with his meditations.

"Two British warships are in pursuit of our ship," Captain Wicks warned him one day. Franklin scanned the horizon for a few minutes, and went back to his serene meditations.

But Captain Wicks was not taking any chances. A bold sea dog, he unleashed his sails, and the *Reprisal,* heaving and rolling on high seas, outsped the British warships. It added excitement to the long and rough voyage. Temple and Ben were lost in admiration of this exploit and never stopped talking about it. They had even more to wonder at when Captain Wicks captured two English merchant ships and brought them into port off the coast of Brittany.

It had been a time of rest for Franklin, even though the ship was uncomfortable and the going rough. But they were all glad to leave the ship at last and continue the journey to Paris by carriage.

At the entrance of the Hotel d'Hamburg, a large crowd was waiting to catch a glimpse of Franklin when he arrived. Everybody in Paris had heard about the great American philosopher; and many of them had read his books: *The Way to Wealth* and *Poor Richard's Almanac.* Men of fashion, in powdered wigs, dressed in velvet and satin, were taken aback when the long-awaited carriage pulled up at the hotel, and they saw Franklin smiling serenely from under a huge fur cap, and iron-rimmed glasses.

"But he wears no wig," exclaimed a young dandy.

"Oh, but certainly. He is a sage, what matters what he wears," reproved an older man, taking snuff out of his gold snuff box.

"He invented the lightning rod. He is a great scientist," another Frenchman broke in. 64049

"Noble savage," exclaimed a lady leaning out of her carriage in passing to take a look at the American.

"But his coat is so plain and brown; it is quite shabby, in fact," whispered an elegantly attired gentleman to his companion.

"He is thinking only of Liberty," explained the other.

"Liberty." The word ran from mouth to mouth like a song as they watched Franklin disappear slowly into the hotel.

Benjamin Franklin loved people, but he was tired. All the way to Paris, wherever he stopped for the night, callers came to question him about the revolution in America, and about the way the war was going, about his views on religion, philosophy and science. He took a hot bath and put on a comfortable dressing gown. He was seventy years old. He had never known a time when he was not beset by one thing or another that he must do. It was pleasant to sit alone quietly for a little while. But first, he opened a box. On top of carefully filed letters and notebooks was a bogus treaty, addressed to King George of England; he was to present this document in case he were captured. He tore the stiff sheet of paper into small scraps and tossed them into the grate.

The Continental Congress of the thirteen American colonies had appointed Franklin to negotiate a treaty of alliance with France. The Congress had also appointed Silas Deane and Arthur Lee on this mission. The portly Mr. Deane met Franklin at Versailles and escorted him to the hotel. There had not been much opportunity for private conversation in the commotion of that meeting; Franklin was therefore delighted when Deane presented himself later in the day. He met Deane with a welcome embrace and closed the door against intruders. Still wearing his dressing gown, a benign expression on his wide face, his fringe of white hair hanging loose, he listened to Deane's report with an air of leisurely interest.

"Louis XVI would like to avenge himself on England for the wretched treaty England forced France to accept at Dunkerque," Deane was saying, and paused to smile wryly. "The word 'Liberty' the king does not seem to fancy."

"No, a king wouldn't," Franklin smiled back.

"Count Vergennes, the king's minister, is eager to see us win our independence from Britain. He wants our trade, and he hopes to get our help to fight against the British when France is ready."

Franklin remained silent, weighing every word.

"France cannot help us openly until we have a victory of sufficient importance to assure them our revolution will be successful," continued Deane. "The news is not good," he added. "Washington has been driven from New York, and he is still retreating. Vergennes is cautious."

"I must see Vergennes," said Franklin quietly.

Temple was to be his grandfather's secretary. Meanwhile the handsome young man, overflowing with high spirits, went out to walk in the streets of the gay city to observe the fashions and to watch the parade of handsome carriages, carrying elegant ladies in hooped skirts of satin and lace, and fantastic hair-arrangement that towered high above their painted faces. He watched the men in flowing powdered wigs, flowered vests and lace ruffles, parading on the boulevard. But there were other streets, Temple soon discovered, crowded narrow streets, where people looked hungry and cold in their ragged garments. Never had he seen such a display of luxury, nor such poverty. It bewildered him. "Why is it like this?" he asked his grandfather.

Franklin shook his head; it was not wise to talk of such matters. The king disliked the word Liberty, and their great philosopher, Voltaire, was writing books that made people think and talk and question the way of things as they were. Rousseau was writing books about the simple life. There would be a day of reckoning sometime; meanwhile young Marquis de Lafayette was taking notice of the American revolution and making plans of his own.

Vergennes invited the three envoys to call at his office at Versailles. Arthur Lee and Silas Deane dressed themselves elaborately after the French fashion. Franklin came out to meet them wearing his old brown coat and his fur cap over his scanty gray locks.

"You are not going like this?" protested Lee.

"Certainly I am," he assured Lee with a smile.

Vergennes seemed entirely oblivious of Franklin's unfashionable attire. "The presence of Monsieur Franklin in Paris will promote the American cause," he assured the Americans. "For the present, caution is better than vigorous speeches."

Franklin bowed as gracefully as his thickset body permitted. He knew that Vergennes was referring to Stormont, the British ambassador who had protested to the French government for permitting envoys from the rebel colonies to enter Paris. He had been amused to hear that Vergennes had assured Stormont that Franklin had come to Paris to attend lectures at the Academy of Science.

"Perhaps," Vergennes continued, smiling that very polite smile of the French, "our meeting may result in more than advice, if you will call on Monsieur Gerard."

Arthur Lee frowned, and bowed stiffly. He expected more than hints from this interview. He complained about it all the way home. Franklin continued to smile in silence. He liked Vergennes, and he felt certain Vergennes meant to be their friend.

Monsieur Gerard received the three Americans a few days later, and though he was as cautious in his manner as Vergennes, he offered to lend Congress two million livres without interest.

"A paltry sum," exclaimed Lee gloomily as they drove away.

"Better than nothing," Deane tried to be cheerful.

Franklin remained silent as he always did when he tried to reason things out in his own mind. He felt grateful for both the interview and the loan. There was nothing they could do to hasten an alliance or a loan until better news came from home. Meanwhile he walked to the Academy daily, tapping the icy sidewalks with his stout stick carved from an apple tree. People stopped their carriages to greet the strange American in his fur cap. Everybody in Paris talked about him. Artists painted his picture and made engravings of him. It became fashionable to have a picture of Franklin over the mantelpiece, and on ladies' fans and snuff boxes, and even on rings.

Too many people came to see him in Paris. He wanted time to meditate and to write. He was delighted, therefore, to move to Passy to occupy a wing in a chateau offered him by one of his admirers; and now that he felt settled for the time being, he made arrangements to send little Ben to school.

Temple, established as his grandfather's secretary, read the letters from Congress, and wondered how his grandfather could remain so serene at such bad news. Washington had been defeated all the way across New York and New Jersey. What was left of his army was encamped at Valley Forge. Winter weather, soldiers with no boots, and no money, and the English boasting of speedy victory.

Vergennes was becoming more and more polite and cautious. Lee took it as a bad sign and complained about it.

The picture was not all dark, however. Beaumarchais, a clever politician and writer, interested in America for his own reasons, organized a company to ship ammunition and weapons to the colonies, and the king was subsidizing this company without anyone knowing it. Ships were secretly dispatched to the West Indies and reshipped from there to the colonies.

But how did the British men of war find out when and where ships sailed? Temple came to his grandfather with information that everybody was talking about spies.

"They can find out nothing of which I am ashamed," Franklin told his grandson with a twinkle of a smile.

"You are surrounded by spies," a friend warned in a letter, and Franklin wrote back ". . . I have long observed a rule . . . to be concerned in no affair that I should blush to have made public . . . If I were sure that my valet is a spy, as he probably is, I think I should not discharge him if . . . I liked him otherwise . . ."

But Young Temple found it difficult not to speculate about who the spies might be. He looked for them everywhere. It never occurred to him that Bancroft, Silas Deane's secretary living with them at Passy, was actually receiving pay from the British chief of spies, Mr. Wentworth. Temple, not too careful a secretary, left his grandfather's papers scattered on the desk where Bancroft could read them if he chose. Bancroft was a pleasant man to talk with and good company. Temple could not know that the chatty letters Bancroft wrote were reports to his chief, written in invisible ink between lines of the letters. Nor did Temple know that these letters were sealed in bottles, and the bottles placed in a hole in a tree on the terrace of the Tuileries. Every Tuesday, at nine thirty, Wentworth's messenger picked these bottles up, and left a message for Bancroft in a similar bottle.

Ships sailing for the West Indies were intercepted by British men of war all too often not to rouse alarm. And yet, though Bancroft was a cunning spy, he found himself at a disadvantage when he listened in on Franklin's conversation. He simply could not believe that this astute philosopher was not hiding anything.

Then one day in January, Franklin received a letter from Congress which sent their hopes soaring—Washington had attacked Trenton, captured the entire Hessian regiment, and all their ammunition. A few weeks later came word that Washington had forced the British to retreat from Princeton to New York. All the papers in Paris were full of accounts of Washington's victories.

This was a good time to talk of a loan. Franklin decided to ask for an interview with the French minister. But Vergennes met the Americans with cautious talk again. "Times are hard," he confided. "The king is pressed for money. If Spain were to join the alliance the king might find ways to make a loan." He bowed the Americans out with one of his most elaborate bows.

"These frog-eaters," cried Lee on the way home from the interview. "The queen is gambling for high stakes to amuse herself. She loses great sums of money and she pretends at the same time that she is leading a simple life in that extravagant villa of hers at Versailles, milking cows and all that kind of rubbish. Every drop of that milk costs the French people a fortune, and the king tells us that he can't afford to give us a loan to fight a just war."

"It will turn out all right, whether they lend us money or not. The less we owe to others, the freer we'll be," reasoned Franklin. But Lee, impatient, left for Madrid to hasten negotiations in Spain.

The good news about Washington's victories were soon forgotten when reports began to circulate that the British general, Burgoyne, was coming down with his army from Canada, and that Howe was threatening to take Philadelphia. "Unless we have help, all is lost," wrote Congress. But no help was in sight, only more bad news: Burgoyne took Ticonderoga. Franklin read these gloomy

letters from Congress and laid them aside as if he did not quite
believe all that Congress seemed to want him to believe. He took
greater care than ever now to appear untroubled. He visited the
Academy and the libraries more frequently to keep himself occupied. He accepted invitations more readily, and appeared at gather-
ings serene and witty. His old friend, Madame Helvetius, invited
learned friends to meet him. His stories delighted them all.

When his anxiety became too great to bear in silence, he relieved
himself by writing witty pamphlets, ridiculing the British for buy-
ing Hessian soldiers to fight their war. Meanwhile, three American
cruisers were fitted out secretly in French ports, and sent out into
the English Channel to do havoc to British shipping.

Stormont protested to Vergennes again. The Frenchman pretended as usual that he knew nothing about the affair, and promised Stormont he would look into it.

The picture looked dark. Franklin refused to accept it and he
had friends who shared his conviction that in the end the Americans would win their freedom. French officers offered themselves
to fight in the American cause—The Marquis de Lafayette, young
and aflame with high ideals, offered himself and his fortune to help
in the struggle for Liberty. He sent gifts of money to the Continental Congress, and offered to equip an army and bring it with
him to America.

Franklin was deeply touched by this generosity ". . . Take
charge of this amiable young nobleman and of his money," he wrote
to Washington. "Advise him, if necessary, with friendly affection,
and secure him from too much imposition . . ."

The hard winter went by slowly; spring bloomed into summer,
and faded into autumn. Another winter came. Franklin read the
desperate letters from Congress and dipped deeper into his own
faith. Failure appeared more certain from day to day. Frenchmen
were shaking their heads. Howe had taken Philadelphia, and
Burgoyne was entrenched on the heights of Saratoga. If Burgoyne
succeeded in cutting off New England from the rest of the country,
and if he joined Howe to march south, that would be the end of

the revolution. Only a large loan and a treaty of alliance with France could save the situation.

"We must ask Vergennes to arrange for a loan of fourteen million livres," insisted Lee, who had returned from Madrid with no promise of a treaty from Spain.

"This is a poor time to ask for loans and propose treaties," reminded Franklin.

"You seem not to realize our plight. It seems to me that you are here for your own amusement," cried Lee, exasperated.

"Well, then, we shall do as you say," Franklin replied quietly.

Once again Lee and Deane dressed in the height of Parisian fashion to call on the French minister. Franklin did not consider this an occasion for wearing anything more festive than his old brown coat and fur cap.

The Frenchman received the American emissaries coldly. "The king is very angry. How came the British to know you offered the king the schooner *Robert Morris?*" demanded Vergennes.

"I know nothing about this gift," exclaimed Franklin, taken aback.

"It is therefore the idea of these gentlemen," sneered Vergennes. "The schooner was to fly the king's flag and carry arms to the colonies under a new name," he explained sarcastically.

"An excellent idea, even though I knew nothing about it," exclaimed Franklin, unable to restrain a smile.

"You may not know about it, but the British do," said Vergennes with icy politeness. "You Americans carry on all your affairs in the open for all the world to know."

"I agree, we need to be more cautious," said Franklin humbly.

It was useless to talk about a loan now; even Lee realized this. All the way from Vergennes' office, Lee and Deane accused each other for the leak and for harboring spies. Franklin listened to them in silence for a while.

"Enough, enough, gentlemen," he cried out at last. "Even if there had been no spy reports, the news from home makes a loan impossible."

It was harder to wait now. On every side the Americans re-

ceived cold glances and shrugs in place of the warm congratulations
they had once received.

"Howe has taken Philadelphia," Monsieur Gerard said to Franklin when they met accidentally.

"I beg your pardon, sir," said Franklin with a gay gesture, "Philadelphia has taken Howe."

Gerard laughed heartily in spite of his intention to appear cold.

It was a bleak December day when Franklin invited a few friends
to take Sunday dinner with him.

Lee came to Passy to relieve his anxiety by quarreling with Silas
Deane about what they had done, or had failed to do. The house
had a cheerful air nevertheless, for Franklin was a genial host. He
told witty stories and droll anecdotes. There was laughter, and good
food. No one could guess how greatly he was troubled in his mind
about the bad news from Congress. Suddenly a loud dispute broke
in upon them from the entry. It was the butler's voice, and the
voice of a stranger arguing with him. The next minute a young
man dashed into the room. His clothes were wrinkled with travel.

"I come from Boston." He spoke hurriedly but his eyes lighted
on Franklin at once. "My name is John Austen," he introduced
himself. "I have important news from Congress."

"Has Howe really taken Philadelphia?" asked Franklin quietly.

"Yes," nodded the young man. "But I have more important news.
General Burgoyne has surrendered at Saratoga with five thousand
eight hundred officers and men, forty-two cannon, five thousand
muskets and stores of ammunition."

Lee jumped from the table and grabbed the young man by the
shoulder. "Is General Burgoyne captured?" he asked.

"Please be calm, Mr. Lee," said Franklin quietly. "Have you
brought a letter from Congress?" he asked the newcomer with a
radiant smile.

"Here are my credentials, sir, and the letter." The young man
handed Franklin the papers. "Burgoyne and his army are our
prisoners."

Franklin read the letter slowly. "We have won a great victory, gentlemen," he said solemnly, and his voice trembled with happiness.

Silas Deane and Lee joined Temple in cross-questioning young Austen, who was only too happy to relate the news over and over again in all its detail.

It soon became apparent that Britain knew what had happened before Franklin heard it. Wentworth, the chief of spies, came hastily to Paris. He was to offer the Americans land titles, money, and privileges, if they would make a treaty of peace with Britain. Franklin, pretending he was interested in Wentworth's conversation, invited him to dinner. He wanted Vergennes to hear that the British were making advances to the Americans. Vergennes did hear of Wentworth's visit. Gerard presented himself a few days later with congratulations. Louis XVI was now ready to sign a treaty and to offer a large enough loan to help the colonies to a final victory.

Smiles greeted the Americans everywhere now and the king received them informally in his dressing room. He was young and fat, and given to being moody, but today he was in good spirits. The treaty had been signed and seals affixed. The king promised his friendship and offered to send what help he could. Vergennes gave a great dinner, and invited all the important nobles to meet the envoys from the savage country.

"I am glad you have at last concluded your mission so successfully," congratulated Monsieur Gerard with a more elaborate bow than ever.

"It was not I who have concluded this alliance; it was the victory at Saratoga," Franklin bowed in return.

"It was your tact and patience that made this treaty come about," explained Gerard.

"It was the victory at Saratoga, monsieur," Franklin said again with a meaningful smile.

A great crowd had gathered to watch the Americans. Franklin, dressed in the blue velvet suit he had been saving for this occasion, carried a white hat under his arm, his head bare. He accepted the greetings and the cheers of the crowd with a childlike good humor.

"The American sage looks more imposing than the nobles," commented a witty Frenchman. Perhaps others were thinking this also, for the cheers grew more enthusiastic as he stood there, bowing right and left.

He was a little tired now and he was thankful that the great day of celebration was drawing to a close. But there was still one more duty to perform before he could go home to his books and meditations; they were to call on the royal family at the palace that evening.

The crowds had gone home at last and it was easier to get about. In the hall of mirrors, candelabra of many candles sparkled with dazzling splendor. The polished floor was slippery. It was difficult to walk without watching each step. The three Americans were glad to enter the carpeted apartment where the queen was playing cards with a group of her young friends.

Marie Antoinette had heard a great deal about the great savage from America. She received him with a gracious smile, and invited him to stand at her side while she continued to play.

How young and pretty she was, glittering with jewels, her wealth of golden hair piled high above her white forehead and entwined with ornaments of precious stones. Franklin smiled down at her benignly. Her blue eyes sparkled with vivacity as she glanced up at him. There was something pitiful and helpless about her he noted. She was gambling for excitement. It seemed not to matter to her whether she lost or won; and she was playing for high stakes.

He also had been gambling for high stakes, but not for a pastime. He watched her a while, thinking of the men and women at home—plain folks in homespun, buckskin breeches and coonskin caps, brave men fighting for liberty, and women watching and praying, building a new world out of their faith and courage. He glanced at Marie Antoinette. She was still smiling as she pushed her losses aside. He was a philosopher, a sage; a great pity for her came to him. She was losing more then she knew, while he and his people were building a new world. He was glad he was an American.

JOHN PAUL JONES

—— *1779* ——

"I have not yet begun to fight."

THE WIND WAS LIGHT, THE SEA CALM. THE CREW
on the *Bonhomme Richard* had plenty of time to keep the ship
tidy and the decks swabbed. No one knew exactly where they were
going. There was some speculation about it, but there was mystery
enough to occupy them all, to keep any from worrying; and be-
sides, the merchant ships, captured since they sailed from the Isle
de Groax, were rich enough prizes to assure everyone of ample pay.

111

Commodore Jones paced the deck with uneasy stride . . . If he could control the wind, he would be nearer his destination. At this rate, all his plans and hopes would come to nothing. He had wasted valuable time waiting for a ship to take him on this expedition, and the *Bonhomme Richard,* named for his beloved friend, Benjamin Franklin, was not a ship to boast about. It was nothing more than an old French merchant vessel that had sailed the Atlantic for many years. He had managed, by ingenuity, to convert her into a warship.

He was not a tall man, but his powerful shoulders and his commanding manner lent him height. His movements were swift and graceful, and his handsome swarthy face had a compelling dignity. Up and down he walked, thinking. Everything seemed to have conspired to delay this expedition—a becalmed sea and then storms. But they were in British waters at last. He looked at the sailors polishing brass and swabbing decks. His crew was mostly French, Portuguese, and British prisoners. But these men were part of his prized American crew: New Hampshire boys, leather skinned and tough, and not a few Nantucket sea dogs, and a few Vermonters learning the game. Jones gave them all a fleeting smile as he went down to his cabin at last, his mind busy with many plans.

On the table of his cabin lay the American flag, carefully folded. Young women of Virginia had made it out of their party dresses and a wedding dress. They had presented this flag to him on the eve of his sailing on the *Ranger.* He spread it out on the table: six white stripes and seven red ones and a wreath of thirteen white stars on a blue field. It stood for a great idea: a new nation, proclaiming that men had inviolable rights. He had flown it on the *Ranger* when he took the *Drake.* But that was only the beginning. A time would come, he vowed under his breath, when this flag would fly high on many a ship, and proclaim to all the world that they were a free nation possessed of a navy to be reckoned with.

Meanwhile, the British were raiding American shores, burning towns, capturing American men and keeping them chained in desolate prisons. His black eyes snapped fire. He paced the floor like a caged panther. He should have a large ship, a mighty fleet. The Continental Congress had promised him a ship worthy of his ability. But nothing had come of that promise—The *Ranger* was needed at home, he was told. All the ships they could get were needed at home to defend their shores; he knew this well enough without anyone telling him. Up and down he walked to calm his thoughts. He had to petition the French king to give him a ship. But the French had, at last, declared war on the British; she also needed all her ships for her own navy.

France did at last give him a ship. Nothing after all could keep him from his rendezvous with destiny. He had, in fact, a fleet of three ships. His lips came together in a hard line. The British prisoners made a poor crew; fifty of them escaped with one of his barges when two of his men took them out to tow the head of the *Richard* to the tide. He had made up for the loss when he captured a coal ship and made more prisoners, but they were a liability in the long run; and his fleet was another liability. He had been obliged to sign a paper which gave each captain under his command permission to do as he chose in his own ship. Captain Landis, of the *Alliance,* the largest of his three ships, was proving himself as unreliable as the British prisoner crew. Jones frowned and stood staring at the flag, as he folded it slowly with a caressing gesture.

The sailors on deck fell into conversation, now that the awesome presence of the commodore was not there—"It don't jest seem as if we're going anywheres," exclaimed the young Vermonter.

"Don't ye worry, my boy," cackled an older sailor, wagging his shaggy head. "If you'd been with us on the *Ranger* you'd know we're going places."

"That so," cried a lean New Hampshire man, shaking out his wet mop. "One of these days we'll be in a scrap that'll keep you runnin' an' fightin'."

"Ay, if you'd been on the *Ranger* when we raided Whitehaven, you'd've seen somethin' worth seein'," burst out a redheaded sailor, hands on his hips.

"Whitehaven?" repeated the Vermonter. "Isn't that where the British have a fort and keep merchant ships under cover?"

"Certainly is, Bob, an' it's a mighty fine fort," the bearded sailor chuckled. "The captain, he thought 'twas good enough for us to look into. So we jest sailed up to the docks, and there was the ships at anchor, fine ships, an' the guns on the fort mighty imposin'," the old sailor bit into a wad of tobacco.

The young Vermonter they all called Bob came nearer. "Was there no guard on the fort?" he asked full of curiosity.

"Ay, there was indeed—The captain got me to stand on Mike's shoulders, an' Nick got on my shoulders, and there we was," cried the redheaded man grinning at the recollection. "The guards jest let out a yell and ran to rouse the town."

"We was to spike the guns with scraps of iron, the commander told us, and we did," chuckled a Nantucket man.

"We might 'ave done a lot more, but 'twas near daylight by the time we was through with the guns," added the New Hampshire man. "We took time though to set fire to the biggest ship, and Nick found a barrel of tar and dumped it into the hold—Did she burn!

"Piff, paff, pft, went the guns when the guard tried to shoot at us. They jest couldn' do a thing!" the redheaded sailor slapped his thighs. "We was back on the *Ranger* before they found out their guns was spiked."

"Captain Jones, he jest stood on the shore his pistol cocked, ready to fire at anyone who came near us," reminisced the New Hampshire man. "The guards on the fort, cursed an' swore an' the people hollered an' yelled and shook their fists; Captain Jones jest laughed, an' waited till every last one of us was back on the *Ranger.* Then he fired his pistol in the air an' rowed back himself. He was the first to come ashore an' the last to leave, jest as he promised."

"What we did to Whitehaven isn't anything to compare to what we did to the *Drake,*" boasted a newcomer.

"You tell us, Nick," called out several mocking voices.

"Never heard neither about Whitehaven nor 'bout the *Drake,*" admitted Bob regretfully.

"The *Drake* had more guns an' more men than the *Ranger,*" said the New Hampshire man. "But my, did we fix her! Never let on who we was; hid our flag an' flew an English flag; had our guns hid too. Captain on the *Drake* he was all for British etiquette," he laughed. "Tried to figure us out, sent a landing boat with a lieutenant and six sailors aboard the *Ranger* to inquire."

"You should've seen that lieutenant, when we took him prisoner," put in Nick. "The captain on the *Drake,* he signaled to her officer; no answer did he get, so the *Drake,* she opened her sails and started for the *Ranger*—You should've been there, Bob." The New Hampshire man winked at the boy good-naturedly. "An' Captain Jones, he jest let the *Drake* chase us clear into the North Channel."

"It's between Scotland and Ireland, in case you want to know," explained the redhead. "She couldn't escape from there."

"Mighty fine boat, had twenty guns; we had only eighteen. She was bigger too; she was a British man of war," chuckled the bearded sailor. "'Let her come within pistol shot,' said Captain Jones. Suddenly the *Drake* hoisted her British flag; we hoisted our stars and stripes in answer. 'What's your ship?' called out the Britisher. 'The American Continental ship the *Ranger;* we're waiting for you to come on,' Captain Jones called back, cool and polite."

"Ay, he can be polite all right," a sailor laughed.

"We was getting our ship in position," interrupted Nick. "Our guns fired a broadside. We jest crippled her from the start."

"She kept on fighting all right, but it was no use; her flag was shot down, her hull was full of holes—That was a fight. We had her prisoner in an hour," boasted the redheaded sailor.

"To think we came near to mutiny when he told us we was to raid the British shores an' attack her shipping," mused the older sailor chewing his tobacco thoughtfully.

"We came mighty near it," reminded Nick. "'We came to sea for profit,' we told him—'We came to raid merchant ships and take prisoners,' we told him—'We ain't gonna risk our necks for nothin',' we told him."

"'Put Captain Jones in chains, we'll do as we please,' said some, an' we came near doing it," nodded the New Hampshire man.

"Ay, an' the captain jest listened quiet like and polite like—But there was a queer look to his eyes—jest froze you cold," said Nick.

"'The British keep our men chained in their stinking prisons,' said he. 'I swore,' said he, 'to fight for the rights of men,' to force the British to give up our men, to make them respect our navy.'"

At this moment John Paul Jones came on deck, followed by Captain Cottineau of the *Palace*. The crew dispersed as if by magic. Jones could be magnanimous, but he gave no quarter to idlers.

The commodore had no eyes for the crew just now. He walked swiftly to the railing and stood there in silence looking through his spyglass. Cottineau looked down over the railing at his own ship, standing nearby.

"How many sails did you say?" Jones asked in a tense voice.

"About forty sails, I believe, bound South by East."

"Must be the Baltic fleet," exclaimed Jones under his breath. "Just what I was hoping for."

By next morning everyone on the *Richard* knew that the Baltic fleet had been sighted. Whispered speculations kept everyone in a fever of expectation the next two days. The *Richard* headed for cover in a quiet bay, the shores of which circled to the north and came to an end in a low headland. The sea sparkled emerald green.

"That's Flamboro Head," figured out a sailor at the rail.

Bob craned his neck, and tried to appraise the distance to the British ships.

" 'Taint much of a wind," old sea dogs wagged their heads, and took generous bites of tobacco to spit over the rail while they waited, and expressed misgivings about the condition of the *Richard:* her old guns and her worn cannon. A sudden shrill note from the boatswain's whistle sent all scurrying to their allotted places. The wind had suddenly come to life, the sails were filling.

"Clear for action," shouted First Lieutenant Richard Dale.

Bob started to fight his way through the mad scramble and gained the forecastle at last, in spite of the pushing and shouting. He climbed the ratlines to the top like an old hand and found his place. The foretop crew was all American; he could see their faces, tough and sure, as they appeared above the foretop flooring.

"Hoist up arms and ammunition," a midshipman was yelling. "Lower away with the rope." Bob peered down at the deck, and saw the sandbags waiting to be hauled up.

"Ahoy, stand by," shouted the midshipman while the sandbags

were being lashed together to form a breastwork. "Look to the muskets," the midshipman was shouting.

Sailors were lugging tubs of water and kegs of powder.

"See if the flints are right in the muskets," roared the midshipman, his voice hoarse with excitement.

On the deck, bellow guns were run out, tompions drawn, tubs set out behind batteries. The French sergeant major of the French marines was calling the roll on the forecastle; the butts of muskets thumped the deck in answer.

Commodore Jones counted the sails from the forepart of the forecastle: forty-one merchant ships, guarded by two men of war. He had a list of all the British ships in his possession. He studied the two frigates as they moved slowly to the head of the fleet. The largest frigate was the *Serapis,* a new ship; she carried fifty guns. The smaller frigate was the sloop of war, *Countess of Scarboro.* He knew also that the merchant ships were carrying valuable lumber and great stores of ammunition. He made his calculations swiftly and formed his plan. If he could rely on Captain Landis to stand by with the *Alliance,* he could be more certain of victory. Captain Cottineau of the *Palace* was at hand, however, and the small cutter the *Vengeance* could help by harassing the *Countess of Scarboro.*

On the *Serapis,* meanwhile, Captain Pearson was taking note of the *Richard,* and signaled hurriedly to the merchant ships to speed to *Scarboro* and seek protection under the Fort guns, while he moved the *Serapis* to stand between the fleet and the strangers.

Jones studied Captain Pearson's tactics, and maneuvered the *Richard* to a position between the *Serapis* and the shore to prevent her escape to the protection of the Fort. There had been a fog in the night and the *Alliance* and the *Vengeance* were hidden somewhere behind that yellow curtain. The *Palace* was with him and the two officers watched the *Serapis* as she moved proudly and slowly.

"If that's John Paul Jones," Captain Pearson of the *Serapis* was saying to his lieutenant as they watched the *Richard* through spyglasses, "we're likely to have trouble."

"I've heard he's the most agreeable sea wolf anyone can hope to meet," remarked the lieutenant.

Captain Pearson pursed his lips and remained staring through his spyglass. "Ay, the accounts of him in the papers after the disaster of the *Drake* were more eulogy than blame," he said dryly.

"They say his father was nothing but a poor gardener, a Scotchman. Jones started out to sea as a cabin boy when he was twelve years old and came to be a captain of a ship at twenty-one," volunteered the lieutenant. "How he came by his learning I don't know. It is known that he has a fine library of books, and he's quite a gallant, they say."

"Whatever he is, and whoever he is," interrupted Captain Pearson tartly, "he fights like a fool, or maybe he's just a genius."

Jones watched the maneuvers of the British ship, and decided that she had an able captain. Captain Cottineau, on the *Palace,* came to the same conclusion before long. "The *Serapis* is new and swift, and she has excellent guns," he confided to his lieutenant.

"Is there any sense to the *Richard* standing up to a British man of war?" asked a second mate of a midshipman.

"Our guns are fit for the scrap heap, nothing but old iron," whispered seasoned sailors, shaking shaggy heads.

Jones was not listening to these whisperings. He moved swiftly from deck to deck, saying a word here and a word there. Stolid New Hampshire boys, salty Nantucket seamen, mountain men from Vermont and from Virginia came alive as he urged them on, charging every one of them with his own fighting spirit. They would fight to a finish, he knew; they would show those Britishers the stuff the American Navy was made of.

It was late afternoon, the flaming sunset was graying slowly. The *Richard* and the *Serapis* were still maneuvering for advantageous positions. At Flamboro, meanwhile, a rumor spread that there was to be a tough sea battle. A crowd had gathered on the shores.

Captain Pearson, certain of his superiority, moved his ship with slow deliberation like a skillful chess player. His entire attention was focused on protecting the merchant fleet.

Jones was not bothered with ordinary tactics. His chief concern at the moment was to find ways to outmaneuver the *Serapis.*

"What ship is that?" challenged Pearson.

"I can't hear what you're saying," Jones called back, steering the *Richard* into the place he wanted.

"What ship is that?" Captain Pearson insisted, and hearing no answer, called a third time—"Answer at once or I shall fire."

In answer, the *Richard* fired a broadside into the *Serapis*.

The *Serapis* roared a broadside into the *Richard* at the same moment. The cannonade all but blasted the *Richard* out of the water. Her secondhand cannon exploded on the lower deck, and her wrecked guns killed the gunner.

"We shall have to rely on our small guns," said Jones to Lieutenant Dale. "Our men must fight from the top part of the ship."

Sailors swarmed to the upper decks shouting curses, egging each other on. They were ready for anything now, for they had a mind to fight. The cries of the wounded added a terrible note to these shouts, but the deafening roar of cannon blotted out the human voices. Jones had lost his commodore's hat. He was besplattered with blood. He paused a moment in the thick of the fight to take stock of the situation. "We have but one chance," he spoke to his lieutenant somberly now. "We must make fast the *Serapis* to the side of the *Richard*. Throw out the grappling lines," he ordered a midshipman.

The sailors on the *Serapis* cut the grappling hooks away every time the men on the *Richard* nearly succeeded in grappling her.

The British ship might get away! Jones calculated this possibility while the guns of the *Serapis* fired broadside after broadside into the *Richard*. The *Richard's* hull was full of holes.

The chief sergeant of the French marines was wounded. "It's all over for the *Richard*," he cried. His marines were ready to give up now. "It's all over, no use to die for nothing," moaned the sergeant. The marines put down their arms.

"All over?" Jones looked amazed. He went from man to man, speaking in French, smiling, his eyes flashed—"Have you forgotten the British atrocities at sea? Have you forgotten the prisoners in chains? Have you forgotten the raids, and the burning homes of helpless people? Have you forgotten we're fighting for liberty?"

The French marines listened to him and rushed into the battle

shouting, "Who said we're done? We're not done until we send them to the bottom of the sea."

Nothing could come of this desperate fighting and dying, Jones knew this well enough, unless he could lash the *Serapis* to the side of the *Richard*. He took the wheel himself and steered the *Richard* towards the enemy. A providential puff of wind helped him. Suddenly the two ships came near enough for the *Richard* to graze along the side of the *Serapis,* the outboard fluke of the *Serapis'* starboard anchor, hooked in the *Richard's* mizzen-chains; instantly Jones and his sergeant lashed the bowsprit of the *Serapis* to the mizzenmast of his own ship.

The sailors on the *Serapis* tried desperately to cut the lashings away, only to be instantly shot. They stopped trying at last; the boats were securely tied, side to side. Jones looked at his handiwork, paying no heed to the bleeding cuts on his hands. His sergeant was moaning and cursing, his hands were cut and bleeding.

"No time for swearing," Jones reminded him. "The next minute we may both be blown into eternity."

The *Serapis* was now firing desperately across the two decks. Jones signaled the marines to shoot with their muskets, while he himself manned a gun and fired into the mainmast of the enemy.

Suddenly the ship *Alliance* appeared. "Now," thought Jones, "the battle will soon be over; the *Alliance* will help us to make a quick end of it." To his amazement, the *Alliance* fired into the *Richard*. "You're shooting into the wrong ship!" shouted Jones.

"You're shooting into the wrong ship!" cried the crew in a rage of indignation.

The *Alliance* fired another broadside into both ships this time and sailed away.

The *Richard* was taking water; the *Serapis* continued to fire into the hull of the *Richard*. A fire broke out on both ships.

"Strike, sir," begged a wounded marine officer.

"Strike? Never!" Everyone on the *Richard* knew now, they must either win or die.

A shot hit one of the pumps and blew it off. "We're sinking," desperate voices cried out to each other. The decks were covered with dead and wounded. Moans and cries filled the air from every side. The master gunner ran aft to haul down the flag.

Captain Pearson, watching from the deck, listened hopefully. "Do you give up?" he shouted.

Jones hurled a pistol at the gunner who dared to think of hauling down the flag, and continued to fire into the *Serapis*.

"Do you ask quarter?" Captain Pearson demanded again.

"I have not yet begun to fight!" Jones shouted in answer.

Pearson rallied his men around him and attempted to get aboard the *Richard,* cutlasses and pistols in their hands. Jones called upon his men to fall upon the invaders and drive them off. But the *Richard* was so full of holes that shots fired into the ship came out into the water from the holes on the other side.

Jones had but one more strategy now. Sailors were sent to hide in the rigging, and hurl lighted grenades onto the deck of the *Serapis*.

British sailors fell like flies, but other sailors came out, and shot into the rigging until the sails of the *Richard* hung in tatters.

The ships were rolling slightly in the swell. Night had come on, and a pale moon stood in the darkling sky. Midshipman Fanning lay crouching in the rigging. Bob, the young sailor, lay behind him.

"We must win," whispered Bob, watching the commodore with awe. He would gladly give his life to help win the battle—What could he do? he asked himself desperately. As if in answer, he heard Fanning say, low under his breath. "Light the grenade."

"Let me throw it," begged Bob eagerly.

"You keep behind me and hold on to the other grenade, and see that you light it quickly, in case we need it," whispered Fanning cautiously. The two crept across the tangled spars into the rigging of the *Serapis*. Fanning grabbed the burning grenade from the boy and flung it into the partly open hatch of the *Serapis*. A terrific explosion deafened everyone aboard both ships.

The *Serapis* shivered and rocked, flames lapped out, and licked her decks. Her mainmast rocked back and forth like a crazy thing ready to topple. The moon was high now, a red tinge on her face, as if she were smeared with blood. It was long after ten o'clock. Commodore Jones, without a trace of fatigue on his swarthy face, was still firing his gun, as if indeed he had just begun to fight. But there was not much left to shoot at though the British flag was still waving proudly in the soft breeze.

Acting Lieutenant Myrant, of Virginia, mustered a party of sailors to rush aboard the *Serapis*. He seemed not to know that his legs were badly wounded and that his face was covered with burns. Captain Pearson saw them coming; he looked around him, his decks were covered with dead and wounded. He climbed up, hauled down the ensign of the *Serapis* and struck his flag.

Lieutenant Dale, standing on the rail of the *Richard,* was preparing in spite of wounds in his leg, to join Myrant on the *Serapis*. Suddenly he heard a great shout. Myrant was calling to him.

"He has struck. Come and take possession."

Dale limped across the deck and bowed courteously to Captain Pearson. "I have the honor, sir, to be Lieutenant Richard Dale . . . of the American Continental ship, the *Bonhomme Richard,* under Commodore John Paul Jones. What ship is this?"

"His British Majesty's late ship, the *Serapis,* sir. I am Captain Richard Pearson," replied the captain sadly. He followed Dale aboard the *Richard,* and surrendered his sword to John Paul Jones.

"You have fought heroically, sir . . . You have worn this sword to your own honor and the honor of your country," said Jones.

Captain Pearson bowed, and remained silent. Jones directed him to escort the prisoner to his cabin.

The *Richard* was filling with water rapidly. The decks were being submerged. Jones commanded that the wounded be transferred to the captive ship, and to the *Palace,* and helped the doctor carry them with tender care. They were his heroes; gladly would he give them his own blood if it would help.

Only the dead were left on the *Richard* at last. The dead, and the flag, still flying bravely in the night breeze. Commodore Jones stood bareheaded on the topmost deck as the *Richard* settled slowly into her rest. Was he praying for those heroic dead who made this victory with him? He was glad that the flag he cherished was still there, going down with them into a gallant grave, a grave that marked the beginning of a great Navy.

ANDREW JACKSON

—— *1834* ——

"Let the people rule."

ROBERT BARTON WAS SORELY DISAPPOINTED. HE
had expected to see an elegant city when he came to Washington,
and he was amazed to find that it looked like an overgrown village.
Only Pennsylvania Avenue, wide and handsome, was paved from
the Capitol to the White House, just one mile. There were a few

elegant mansions on the avenue, but on the mud-rutted roads there were only shabby farmhouses with vegetable gardens, and cattle grazing in the fields. He felt homesick and lonely. The crowds on the street were as disappointing as the city: gloomy, worried faces, shabby men standing about in groups arguing and disputing.

He was glad to enter Gadsby's Inn where his uncle, William Barton, was waiting for him. "You're late, Bob," said his uncle after a few words of greeting, "I was about to go in to dinner without you."

"I am sorry, Uncle Bill," apologized Bob. "Went sightseeing, and I guess I walked too far."

"Well, no matter, we are just on time," said Mr. Barton.

The long tables in the dining room were already filled by the time Mr. Barton and his nephew found their allotted places.

Robert looked about him with deep curiosity. This was his first dinner at the famous Gadsby's Inn. These were the great ones and their wives, dressed in extravagant fashion, talking gayly, exchanging compliments and bits of gossip—the politicians and statesmen who shaped the course of events.

"My nephew's come to Washington to become a newspaper man," William Barton introduced Robert around the table with a little wave of his hand.

"Excellent, we need new writers," cried friendly voices.

Robert felt shy in spite of the welcoming words. Only a few places away, he recognized the stern face and the piercing black eyes of Calhoun, and farther up the table he saw the dark scraggly head, topped by jet black hair, of the great orator, Daniel Webster. And that must be Senator Clay, sitting next to Webster, decided Robert, glancing shyly towards the graceful figure lounging in his chair, his gray eyes twinkling with amusement.

"A newspaper man should know everybody and talk to everybody," Mr. Barton was saying. "I'll introduce you to Duff Green, editor of the *United States Telegraph*. Write something meanwhile so we can show it to him."

"That's what I'd like to do, but I don't know what to write about yet," confessed Robert.

"Listen to what people say," advised his uncle, and turned to converse with the man on the other side of him.

Robert tried to make out what the conversation was about. All he was able to gather was that everyone was angry about something.

"The country is in a panic, sir, the worst panic we ever had," remarked the man across the table.

"That's to be expected," exclaimed Clay. "When Andrew Jackson refused to recharter the bank, some of us knew that trouble was in the making—The whole country is affected by the Bank of the United States."

"The ignorant mobs elected Jackson president, and he's catering to the mob," broke in a courtly looking gentleman in a high cravat.

"Ay, and he's turned the White House into a hunting ground for them," agreed a man in a green broadcloth coat.

"The country is ruled by newspaper editors he's put in office. There's scarcely a gentleman in office nowadays," exclaimed the man across the table.

"Not quite as bad as that," interposed a sedate gentleman in spectacles. "It's true that Amos Kendal is an ex-newspaper man, but he's smart, mighty smart."

"Amos Kendal nursed the whole idea of destroying the Bank of the United States," said the man in the high cravat.

"Ay, and it's Amos Kendal who advised Old Hickory to withdraw the government deposits from the Bank of the United States," said the man in the green coat.

Servants brought in steaming platters of meat and fowl, and all conversation stopped for the time being.

"Is all this true, what they said about President Jackson?" asked Robert when he was alone with his uncle at last.

"True enough, my boy, Andrew Jackson is a common man, an ignorant fellow, and a stubborn one. He was elected by the ignorant mobs, and he's trying to please the common people."

Robert went to bed greatly troubled in his mind. If what was said at the table was true, something had to be done to save the country from ruin. He lay awake thinking of articles he would write about it for the *United States Telegraph*.

"Excellent, excellent," exclaimed his uncle when Robert told him his plans at breakfast. "I'll introduce you to the editor this very morning. He may give you a trial assignment."

The office of the *United States Telegraph* was a busy place, with men writing at desks, and messenger boys coming and going. Duff Green received his visitors with breezy politeness. "I've brought you a budding editorial writer," said William Barton with a wide smile, as he introduced Robert.

"We always need good newspaper men," said Duff Green in a noncommittal voice as he glanced at Robert's blushing face with an appraising eye. "The fact is, we need mighty keen men to write in our newspapers nowadays considering what's going on." His hand moved restlessly among the papers on his desk, and Robert's eye fell on a check signed Nicholas Biddle. It was a check for a large sum of money, Robert noted and he looked away quickly, ashamed.

"How is he to begin?" asked the older man.

"Well, supposing you visit the Senate this morning," said Duff Green. "Senator Clay is going to speak. Listen to him carefully, observe the people in the gallery, try to hear what they say. Write a story and bring it to me, and we'll see."

"Perfect," cried William Barton. "You can't make a better beginning, my boy." He shook hands with Duff Green elaborately.

"I expect a good story," said Green to Robert as he ushered them out of his office.

The crowds in the streets did not bother Robert so much today, now that he had his mind fixed on what he was going to do. "Is Washington always as crowded as this?" he asked a chubby little man who was standing alone, watching the churning crowds.

"Never saw so many strangers in Washington," confided the man. "It's on account of the bank trouble. Many of these people are delegates from all over the union, come to petition the president to recharter the bank."

"Does the president listen to their petitions?" asked Robert.

"Old Hickory receives every delegation, and he listens to what everyone has to say." The little man looked questioningly at Robert. "Are you on one of these delegations by any chance?"

"No, indeed," said Robert. "I've not come to Washington to see the president, but to write about him."

"I see," said the little man, examining Robert from head to foot with an appraising eye—"Just out of college, I can see that," the man chuckled. "And what, may I ask, is your line? What do you aim to write about?"

"The country is in a panic; men are out of work, people are starving," cried Robert. "It's all Andrew Jackson's fault, they say. That's what I aim to write about," said Robert.

"Nicholas Biddle is the man you should write about," said the little man. "It's he who is to blame for the panic."

"Nicholas Biddle?" echoed Robert—where had he seen that name, he wondered, and remembered the check on Duff Green's desk. "Who is Nicholas Biddle?"

"Biddle is the president of the Bank of the United States. He's a smart man, loves books and poetry, and he knows his way about in politics also. He is a mighty powerful man, is Czar Nick."

"How can he do all this?" asked Robert incredulously.

"Well, when he wants a man elected to office, he gets his lieutenants to root for the man, and generally the man he wants is elected. Biddle is generous when he wants things done his way. Many's the man in high position gets checks from Biddle. And it's the same with business. Many is the man that's been stopped in politics and in business, too, by Czar Nick."

"That can't be so, sir. I've not heard anyone say any such a thing," cried Robert indignantly.

"Maybe not, young man, but you will before you're much older. For it's Biddle who is responsible for the panic. He froze assets—there's no money in circulation, that's the reason business is failing. When business fails, there's no work; and when there's no work, men go hungry. That's why it's called a panic."

"But, why would Biddle want to do such a terrible thing?"

"Well, it's this way. Old Hickory is on to Biddle, and he's decided that Biddle has taken on too much power for the good of the country, so he refused to recharter the Bank of the United States. The charter is about to expire. Without a charter the Bank

of the United States can't go on. Biddle wants that charter re-
issued; Jackson refused. Biddle started up a powerful campaign
against the president to bring pressure on him. Many a man in
the government is receiving fat checks from Biddle to plague the
president. But so far, Old Hickory is holding out, and what's more,
he has ordered the government deposits transferred to state banks.
When that began to happen, Biddle started to make trouble—business can't go on without credit or currency. Yessir, and so now we
have this panic."

"That's ridiculous," cried Robert. "I heard an entirely different
story about it all." He began to walk very fast towards the Capitol.

The wide stone steps leading to the Capitol were crowded with
loiterers of every description. Elegantly dressed gentlemen in
broadcloth coats, high cravats and gold-headed canes were convers-
ing amiably in small groups; while shabby men with scraggly
beards, unwashed faces, and sullen eyes were muttering among
themselves. There was a sense of disturbance in the air as if thunder
clouds were about to explode into a mighty storm. Robert watched
the scene for a while. In the distance he could see the peaceful
hills of Virginia, steeped in a silver mist. At the back of the
Capitol the Potomac rushed on as if in a hurry to steal away from
it all. And on either side of Pennsylvania Avenue stretched the
unfinished city. What the chubby little man told him haunted
Robert and angered him more and more as he thought of it, and
added to his desire to write a story to expose Andrew Jackson.

The strangers' gallery was full of visitors, and Robert was surprised to see almost as many women as men. He found himself
a place in a corner near the front, from where he could look down
onto the Senate floor. To his amazement he saw women there
also, in large plumed hats and voluminous silk gowns. He leaned
over the railing for a better view of Vice-President Martin Van
Buren, sitting on the rostrum, stiff and erect. Behind him loomed
the six dark marble columns, and overhead the golden eagle spread
his wings as if in warning, or perhaps in protection. Robert liked
to wonder about such things, and to write about things others did
not notice.

Senator Clay was talking on the floor of the Senate. His voice had a silvery ring to it. He spoke with passion; now and then, his voice became low and charged with tears. ". . . To you, sir, in no unfriendly spirit . . . I make this appeal."—Robert listened with deep attention so as not to lose a word.— Now, at last, he would get the facts for the story he was planning to write ". . . tell him of the tears of helpless widows no longer able to earn their bread . . ."

"He wants the Vice-President to tell the President what he is saying," whispered an elderly man with a low chuckle.

"Do you think he will, sir?" asked Robert eagerly.

"I doubt it," said the man. "Clay is rooting for the Bank. Some of the senators are for the recharter. Clay is a good orator. He can melt a stone to tears, but he'll have a hard time to convince the Red Fox that the Bank of the United States is good for the nation."

"The Red Fox?" repeated Robert, with a puzzled look.

"I mean Van Buren, his nickname," explained the elderly man.

Clay was through talking, and was lolling in his seat now. There was a moment of silence. Van Buren stood up, and called a senator to take his place in the Speaker's chair.

A quick buzz of whispers rumbled through the Senate chamber. The Vice-President walked leisurely towards Clay—"May I borrow a pinch of your excellent snuff, sir?" he said with an elaborate bow.

Amazed and startled, Clay looked at Van Buren in silence for a while and handed him his snuff box. Van Buren took a pinch of snuff, sneezed loudly and returned the snuff box to Clay with a deep bow. Then he walked slowly back to the rostrum.

A titter of low laughter rustled through the gallery. Loud hisses of "Shhh" silenced them. A loud argument broke out on the floor of the Senate, and turned into denunciations. Robert could hardly make out what anyone said. Suddenly one of the senators called for a vote.

"What are they voting for?" Robert asked the bearded man at his side.

"The senators are taking a vote to put the stigma of censure against the president," explained the elderly man.

"Are they going to impeach him?" asked Robert greatly excited.

"They wouldn't dare," the elderly man shook his head, a queer smile on his face. "The country is behind Andrew Jackson; they know it, and he knows it. Andrew Jackson thinks he is right about the bank, and maybe he is," added the man with a shrug.

"And how about the Vice-President?" asked Robert uneasily. "He didn't answer Clay's speech."

"Van Buren is with the president. He's just made it clear. Clay's speech wasn't worth more than a pinch of snuff. That's his answer to Clay."

"It's a queer way to answer, sir, no wonder they call him the Red Fox," said Robert, quite bewildered now.

"Well, maybe he is a red fox," smiled the bearded man. "At least he is not taking checks from Biddle for his opinions, as some people do."

"Do you mean to say that Senator Clay takes checks from Biddle for his opinion?" demanded Robert with a frown.

"That's the rumor, young man."

"I don't believe it," said Robert hotly. "Everybody knows Clay is a great man, and everybody knows that Andrew Jackson is trying to ruin the Bank of the United States in order to please the mobs."

"Young man," said the elderly man in a kindly voice. "You seem to be interested in what's going on. I would advise you, therefore, to hear both sides and then form your opinion."

"That's exactly what I would like to do," cried Robert. "What is your opinion about the bank situation, sir?"

"The Secretary of the Treasury, Roger Taney, said something I agree with," the elderly man looked thoughtfully at Robert. "It may help you to understand the situation better if I quote him. 'It is the fixed principle of our political institutions,' said Taney, 'to guard against the accumulation of power over persons and property in anyone's hands. And no hands are less worthy to be trusted with power than the moneyed corporations'—and that, young man, is what's the trouble now. Nicholas Biddle has accumulated power, and he is abusing it."

"Is power to be entrusted to the mobs, sir?" asked Robert smartly.

"You've asked a good question, young man," smiled the older

man. "It is said we are in the midst of a revolution, and that the country is on the brink of a precipice with a panic going on now. They blame Jackson. They call him a reckless tyrant"—

"Well, it's true, isn't it?" asked Robert.

"We are going through a difficult time. It's nothing but the growing pains of democracy," said the man with a whimsical smile. "The common people are waking up to what democracy is, and Jackson is their choice because he has the spirit to fight for it. That is one side. The other side says—'The mobs don't know what's good for them. They are too ignorant to understand government. Power and authority,' they say, 'must ever remain in the hands of the good and the wise and the wealthy to stabilize the country'— these are the arguments of each side."

"And on what side are you, sir?" asked Robert, thinking again of the check he saw on Duff Green's desk. A great determination came to him to find out the truth about it all.

"I am an observer, young man, I offer no opinions," he smiled and moved to go.

"Can anyone get into the White House, sir?" asked Robert.

The man looked at Robert in silence for a moment. "I think so," he said after a while. "You might follow one of the delegations. They always get in." He nodded towards a group of men at the foot of the stairs. "These men, I happen to know, are from New York. If I am not mistaken, they are about to march to the White House. If you follow them, you will no doubt be admitted with them," the elder man looked challengingly at Robert, and walked away with a friendly wave of his hand.

Never in his life had anything seemed so important to Robert, nor as exciting. He attached himself to the delegation with a casual air, and the delegates were too deeply engrossed in conversation to notice him. The mile to the White House did not take long. The delegates pushed through the crowds of loiterers with small ceremony. In front of the White House another crowd was churning and milling about, wild and rough looking men, they seemed to Robert. The president's mobs, he thought.

An important looking gentleman received the delegation at the door with a bow and handshakes. A Negro servant went into an inner room and came out presently—"Enter, please," he said, leading the visitors through the open door. Robert went in with them hoping he would not be noticed.

The president was sitting at his desk, writing and smoking a pipe, taking no notice of the callers.

"Ahem," coughed the important looking man who had welcomed the delegates into the White House. Andrew Jackson continued to write as if he had not heard. After a few minutes, having finished what he was writing, he laid down his pen and looked up with a gracious smile. The polite gentleman introduced the delegates to the president with a formal bow.

"What is your pleasure, gentlemen?" asked the president.

"We need relief, sir, all the money is tied up; credit is gone, business is failing everywhere," said the leader in a complaining voice.

"Go to Nicholas Biddle. He has all the money. We have no money here, gentlemen. Biddle has millions of specie in his vaults, lying idle this very moment, and you come here to me to save you from breaking," exclaimed the president, indignantly.

The delegate tried to speak, to finish his prepared petition, but Andrew Jackson gave him no chance to say another word. The man backed out of the room at last, pale and shaken. His companions followed him, shaking their heads and mumbling angrily.

Robert remained standing pressed against the wall. He felt angry. He hated Andrew Jackson, he told himself. No wonder people hated him, no wonder people talked about him——

The president was standing in the middle of the room: tall and very slender, his mane of white hair piled thick above a high forehead, his deep-set gray eyes full of fire. There was a smile on his lips, a peculiar smile, impish and playful. The man who had gone out after the delegates came into the room again. "Didn't I manage them well?" he asked the man, chuckling.

The man smiled back and chuckled with him. "There's another delegation, sir, from Philadelphia."

"Let them come in, let them come in, let them talk."

Robert pressed closer to the wall, hardly daring to breathe for fear of being detected. A gentleman in a handsome cravat and a tall hat entered, a number of men less elegantly attired with him.

Jackson bowed, dignified and serious again—"Your pleasure, gentlemen," he said cordially.

"The country, sir, is on the brink of ruin," began the man from Philadelphia solemnly. "Recharter the bank, sir, and restore the government deposits. Save us from ruin."

"Restore Nicholas Biddle to power?" exclaimed the president with instant ire—"Andrew Jackson would never restore the government deposits to the bank. Andrew Jackson would never recharter the monster of corruption . . . sooner than live in a country where such powers prevailed, he would seek an asylum in the wilds of Arabia."

At this moment a burst of loud singing rang out in the street—

> "We are a hardy freeborn race,
> Each man to fear a stranger;
> Whate'er the game we join in chase,
> Despoiling time and danger,
> And if a daring foe annoys,
> Whate'er his strength and forces,
> We'll show him that Kentucky boys
>   Are alligator horses.
> Oh Kentucky, the hunters of Kentucky
> Oh Kentucky, the hunters of Kentucky"

The singing died out. "My Kentucky boys," exclaimed Andrew Jackson. He turned to the delegates with a radiant smile—"Fighters," he chuckled triumphantly. "We didn't give up—"

"Sir," exclaimed the gentleman from Philadelphia. "We are come to present our case. I tell you, sir, we're facing ruin. Failure in business everywhere."

"Go to Biddle," cried Jackson. "He created the panic. 'Tis absolutely unnecessary. The failures are among the stock jobbers, brokers and gamblers—Go to Nicholas Biddle, tell him your tales."

"We protest, we rebel, sir, recharter the bank, restore deposits,"

cried the man from Philadelphia.

"If that is your game," exclaimed Jackson hotly, "come with armed bank mercenaries, and I will hang you around the Capitol on gallows higher than Haman's."

The man from Philadelphia faced the president in silence now, his face white and his eyes sullen. Reading the inexorable expression in Jackson's eyes, he turned about and walked out, his men straggled out after him.

Robert, standing against the wall, stared at the president.

Jackson noticed him now—"What have *you* to say, sir?" he demanded abruptly.

"I, sir?" Robert's voice was hardly audible. "I wanted to find out."

"Find out what?" asked Andrew Jackson haughtily.

"The truth," blurted out Robert. "The truth about you, sir."

"The truth about me?" Jackson chuckled. "And why do you want to know the truth about me?"

"I want to write about things, I want to write what's true."

"I see," said Jackson. A warm smile lit up his pale face, and made it shine as if a lamp were lit behind his eyes. "You heard the Kentucky boys singing outside there—Some of them know me; they know what's true about me—We licked the British together when everybody was thinking of giving up." There was a gay ring in his voice now, as if he were a mere young man Robert's age and not a president with a great burden on his shoulders. "They call me a tyrant; you've probably heard what people say about me."

"Yes, sir," admitted Robert.

" 'Tis true I am a tyrant; I give no quarter when the safety of the union is in danger. I give no quarter, when men seek to exercise power taken from the rights of the people."

A servant brought in a tray with refreshments and passed it around. Jackson sat down and relit his long-stemmed pipe, and waved a hand indicating a chair for Robert. He seemed in a genial mood, puffing at his pipe, looking at Robert with a quiet smile.

Robert sat down respectfully on the edge of the chair. "And the bank, sir?" he asked after a silence.

"The bank is to serve the people. That's the true purpose of a bank, my friend," said Jackson, puffing at his pipe. "Biddle took the prerogative to use the power of money to tamper with business, sway opinions, shape politics, influence voters, holding with a few others, that the learned and the rich must remain in power and rule the unlearned and the poor. Only the rich are wise and good, these gentlemen maintain. To such as these I am a tyrant, and I mean to remain so while I hold office."

"You are against the rich and the educated?" Robert asked.

"I am against the unscrupulous and the selfish, that's a more proper way to put it." Jackson puffed at his pipe vigorously; white smoke rose from the bowl and curled in a thick mist around the strange face, so strong and yet so gentle. He seemed fragile as he sat there relaxed, his long fingers holding the bowl of his pipe on his knee.

A great desire to understand him and to serve him came to Robert. "I aim to be a newspaper man, sir, I want to write what's true about the bank and about you, sir," he exclaimed. "I shall go to Duff Green on the *Telegraph* and tell him the truth about the bank. I understand it now, sir. I hope I can make it clear that it's not the bank you're against, it's not Biddle you're against; it's the danger that might overtake our country if money had more power than people. Isn't that what you mean, sir?"

Jackson nodded slowly, puffing at his long-stemmed pipe. "Not Duff Green on the *Telegraph,* my friend," he took the pipe out of his mouth to say presently. "Duff Green is a Biddle man; he would only throw your offering into the waste paper basket. Go to Francis Blair, on the *Globe,* tell him I sent you." Again he puffed at his pipe in silence a while, smiling as if he were seeing something in his thoughts that pleased him—"So long as we have young men who understand the true state of affairs, we shall win this fight," he exclaimed triumphantly.

"Thank you, sir," Robert stood up now, guessing it was time to go.

Andrew Jackson took his hand and shook it warmly. "I'm mighty glad you came to see me. We'll win, my friend," he chuckled, "we'll win."

ABRAHAM LINCOLN

—— *1863–4* ——

"... *It is for us, the living, rather, to be dedicated here to the unfinished work which they who fought here have thus far so nobly advanced.*

... that this nation, under God, shall have a new birth of freedom; and that government of the people, by the people, for the people, shall not perish from the earth."

THE STREETS OF WASHINGTON WERE CROWDED;
soldiers, sailors, officials of every kind and visitors from far and near

came and went as if searching for something, no one knew what. Young Henry Green looked down at his brand new uniform with distaste. He was a soldier now; it was inevitable; all his friends and associates had enlisted. He had to do it, though he had been brought up to consider war wrong. He would have to carry a gun, he would have to kill or be killed.

At a meeting of the abolitionists the day before, his Uncle Warner talked fervently against the need of this war. If the president issued a proclamation abolishing slavery, he argued, the war would end. Two young soldiers in stained uniforms passed him. One had his head bandaged, the other hobbled on crutches. "There's old Abe!" exclaimed the soldier with the crutches.

A tall man with stooped shoulders was walking down Pennsylvania Avenue. Henry stopped to watch him. Was this the president, he wondered. Never had he seen a face so sad and so marked with care, and eyes that looked like wells of sorrow.

Abraham Lincoln gave Henry a friendly smile as he passed him, and stopped to say something to the two soldiers. His face lit up with a momentary flash of light as he spoke to them. Strange thoughts came to Henry as he stood there watching the lanky figure walk away, the guard at his heels.

"Poor old Abe," exclaimed the bandaged soldier. "He's taking it harder than us. All we have to do is fight, and die maybe, but he has the responsibility of the war and of us all."

"Why doesn't he stop the war then? Why doesn't he free the slaves? That would end the war," broke in Henry.

The two soldiers looked at him with a mixture of scorn and pity. "One of those abolitionists!" sniffed the soldier on crutches. "Well, we ain't fightin' to free niggers."

"Then what's this war about?" demanded Henry.

"Brother," cried the bandaged soldier, "maybe you haven't heard that the South decided to secede from the Union, and fired on Fort Sumter. That's what the war is about. We're fighting rebels so as to save the Union. Put that in your pipe and smoke it before you go to the front."

At the White House, the president was holding a meeting with his cabinet. None of the members of the cabinet knew why they had been called. They gathered around the table, grave and serious. Their broadcloth coats and snowy linen, and their well-groomed hair and beards added a touch of elegance to their dignity, which contrasted strangely with Lincoln's indifference to his dress and grooming. His deep-set eyes had a sad and faraway look, as he sat there looking at them, as if he were seeing something none of them knew about. Suddenly a smile played in his weary eyes—"Artemus Ward sent me his book. I will read you a chapter," he drawled. And without waiting to hear a reply, he began to read in a droll voice.

"Showed my show in Utiky . . . a truly grate sitty . . . the people gave me a cordyal resepshun . . . 1 day as I was givin a descripshun of my Beests and Snaiks . . . what was my scorn & disgust to see a big burly feller walk up to the cage containin my wax figgers of the Lord's Last Supper, and cease Judas Iscariot by the feet and drag him out on the ground. He then commenced fur to pound him as hard as he cood. 'What under the son are you abowt?' cried I. Sez he, 'What did you bring this pussylanermus cuss here for' . . . Sez I 'You egrejus ass, that air's a wax figger—a representashun of the falce 'Postle.' Sez he, 'That's all very well fur you to say, but I tell you, old man, that Judas Iscariot can't show hisself in Utiky with impunerty by a darn site!' with which observashun he kaved in Judassis hed. . . . I sood him, and the joory brawt in a verdick of Arson in the 3rd degree—" Lincoln looked up, the smile still playing in his eyes. Only Seward laughed, Chase smiled coldly, and Stanton glowered at him in gloomy silence.

Lincoln laid the book aside and straightened himself in his chair. His face took on the habitual grave look—"I have got you together to read to you what I have written down," he said in a tense voice. "I do not wish your advice about the main matter; for that I have determined for myself . . . I already know the views of each on this question. They have been therefore expressed and I have considered them as thoroughly and as carefully as I can. What I have written is that which my reflections have determined me to say . . ." He studied the faces around the table in silence a moment. He had

read that bit of foolery by Artemus Ward to break down the wall
of fears and doubts by a hearty laugh between them— He began
now to read his final draft of the Proclamation for Abolition of
Slavery. He read it slowly, in a deliberate manner, commenting on
each statement as he read it—The war for the Union would go on,
efforts to buy slaves in states or part of states in rebellion against the
United States, would go on.—"All slaves in states or parts of states
in rebellion, shall, on January 1st, 1863, be thenceforward and forever free . . ." he laid the paper on the table and looked sharply at
his Secretary of State Seward— "When I proposed this proclamation
in July, I agreed with you then that it would not be expedient to
publish the proclamation at a time when McClellan's campaign
failed to take Richmond."

"With the Battle of Antietam we now have a victory," remarked
Seward.

The faces around the table relaxed as they talked about it. It was
not a great victory. It was very small, in the face of all the losses.

"The action of the army against the rebels has not been quite
what I should like," said Lincoln heavily. He sat silent awhile
thinking, looking past the faces around him as if they were not
there—"I made a promise to myself and to my Maker that when
the rebel was driven out of Frederick, I would issue the Proclamation of Emancipation. The rebel army is now out of Maryland.
Pennsylvania is no longer in danger of invasion. I have made up
my mind to issue the proclamation."

There was much talk on street corners, around dinner tables,
offices, and factories when the proclamation was printed in the
papers two days later. Soldiers read the proclamation, and asked,
"Is it to free niggers we're fighting?"

Anti-abolitionists went about accusing Lincoln of dishonesty,
trickery, stupidity, and all kinds of evil intentions.

Mrs. Green read the proclamation aloud—it sounded good but
she was not quite satisfied. "The proclamation frees slaves of
rebels. That's all well enough."

"It is a good way to start," said Mr. Green. "If the freed slaves
are settled in colonies in Haiti and Liberia as the administration

plans, it will be good for them, and for us all."

"But what of the slaves of the Union men? They will still remain slaves?" expostulated Mrs. Green. She was an abolitionist and a Quaker. She was torn between a desire to see slavery abolished and a dread of the war. And now, her son was in it. "This abolition doesn't free all slaves. Why?" she asked uneasily.

Mr. Green remained silent, weighing her question. He was not a Quaker, but he was for abolition. He didn't want his only son to go into the war, and yet, he was glad that Henry would have a hand in this fight for freedom—"The president would free all the slaves if he had it in his power. A man who knows Lincoln's private views told me that," said Mr. Green. "But if he freed the slaves of the Union men now, most of them would join the rebels. A slave is property."

"Property!" Henry glanced at Nancy sitting there so quietly. What was she thinking, he wondered. He had intended to ask her to marry him as soon as he was out of college. Now he would not ask her until he came back from the war; if he came back with both his legs and hands, and his head whole. No, he would not have her think she had to marry a maimed man just because she had made a promise. Was she thinking of that? he wondered.

"The proclamation is wonderful," Nancy said, as if guessing his thoughts. "I walked past a Negro church the other day—There was shouting and singing going on, so I went in to hear what their preacher was telling them."

"Did they let you come in?" wondered Mrs. Green.

"They were too excited to take notice of me," smiled Nancy. "'God saved Moses from the crocodiles,' the preacher was saying. 'God reared Moses up to lead his people to freedom,' he shouted. 'God raised up Massa Lincum and preserbed him, so Massa Lincum might give the black man freedom.'"

"They are right," said Mrs. Green.

"They are so sure of it, it is wonderful," said Nancy. "They all knelt down and prayed and sang 'God bless Massa Lincum.'"

"This is history, what's happening now," exclaimed Henry after a long silence. "It'll change everything for us all. I'll be thinking of that when the bullets fly around me," he added. "I only hope they'll be freed in the entire country." He went out to walk with Nancy under the stars. He would be going away tomorrow. He felt happier, now he knew how Nancy felt about it.

Mrs. Green watched her son from the porch as he walked down the path early the next morning to join the band of recruits on the street. Her eyes were full of tears—"'Tis not to be a soldier we raised our boy," she whispered.

"No," agreed Mr. Green. "But we did pray that he'd take the side that's good and right in life," he reminded her.

Abraham Lincoln, pacing the floor of his office at the White House, was thinking of boys like Henry Green on the battlefield, giving their all—God grant it was not to be for nothing. His proclamation had stirred up new hate and new abuse for him. But the great and liberal thinkers praised him. Emerson praised him. The newspapers praised him. "Grand," "Historic," some of the papers called the proclamation.

"I am receiving enough praise to please any vain man," he said wryly. But praise was not what he was looking for, though he wanted to know that the country was with him. He needed friends, for he had many enemies. And Europe? his proclamation had made a stir there also. Perhaps now, the English Parliament would stop making secret preparations to send her navy to aid the rebels. And France! the French Premier had sent word, offering to mediate between the South and the North, as if they were two countries instead of one—"I am busy putting down a rebellion," he told the Frenchman. Perhaps France would now understand his answer. Up and down he walked, thinking—If only he had more able generals, if only the soldiers stopped deserting.

He went to the Soldiers' Home, three miles out of the city, to talk to the old veterans, and to forget the present for the time being. A young soldier, recuperating from wounds in his legs, was hobbling around on crutches. "How do the soldiers in your regiment feel about the proclamation?" Lincoln asked the boy.

"I'm for it, sir," the young soldier told him eagerly. "But some

of the soldiers say that if they had known the war was to free slaves, they wouldn't have enlisted, so they're deserting. Others say they'll not desert, neither would they fight. They apply for positions in the wagon trains or ambulances."

"Tell the boys, we're fighting to save the Union. We must free the slaves so as to make the Union strong," Lincoln told the boy.

It was New Year's Day. Mr. and Mrs. Green came to the White House to wish the president a Happy New Year. They felt somewhat lost, standing in line. It was a long line; all kinds of people were there: diplomats from foreign countries, officials and office holders, Navy men in brass, military men, soldiers, sailors, ladies in hooped skirts, gentlemen in tall hats, and the great public, folks dressed in their holiday best. Today there was to be no politics, only a pleasant exchange of greetings and hearty handshakes.

Lincoln's large gnarled hand was beginning to feel limp as the morning advanced and the handshaking went on. Today was the day he had set for signing the proclamation of Emancipation. Perhaps he was thinking of that as he gave out compliments and shed smiles with that far-off look in his eyes. No one seemed to believe that he would actually sign that proclamation.

He will change his mind. He will withdraw that proclamation, prophesied those who always doubted him. But there were those others who said Abe Lincoln has grown into fuller stature since he came to office; he knows his mind. He is only slow about signing it because he wants to be sure the Nation would not be permanently torn asunder by it.

But at last the handshaking was over, the carriages departed, the footsteps died away on the walks. He could be alone in his office to think his thoughts. It was nearly five months since the proclamation was published in the papers. It had made the South fight more determinedly while his own soldiers deserted. What if it lead to defeat, and a divided nation with slavery a constant threat of war?

Seward found him pacing up and down when he came to the White House that afternoon with the Emancipation Proclamation, now duly engrossed by the State Department. He spread it out on the table before Lincoln. It needed only the president's signature.

"I never in my life felt more certain that I was doing right, than I do in signing this paper," said Lincoln.

Seward handed him the steel pen that had been bought especially for signing the proclamation.

Lincoln dipped the pen into the inkwell and glanced at the broad sheet of paper spread out before him on the table. A shadow of a smile came into his eyes. "I have been shaking hands since nine o'clock this morning," he looked up at Seward irresolutely. "My arm is stiff and numb. This signature is one that will be closely examined, and if they find my hand trembled, they will say, 'he had compunction.' But any way," he added in a resolute voice, "it is going to be done." The pen moved slowly, forming each letter with care—Abraham Lincoln. The proclamation was signed. The signature looked slightly tremulous in spite of all his carefulness.

"It is a better signature than I expected, after the way your fingers have been squeezed by thousands of hands," said Seward, signing his name. The great seal was affixed. Lincoln watched the procedure in silence. In his youth he had grieved that he had done nothing to make any human being remember that he had lived. He had longed to link his name with events in the interest of his fellow men. Now, his great desire had come to pass—this document linked his name to posterity. To thousands upon thousands it proclaimed that they were free men and women.

The entire city of Washington seemed to have come out into the streets to stand around and talk. Not since that rainy day in November, when Lincoln was re-elected president for a second term, had there been so much excitement in the air—History was taking long strides. The proclamation for abolition of slavery reposed peacefully in the archives of the State Department; and now, the second act of the great drama was to be enacted—The Constitution of the United States was to be amended, in order to make slavery illegal in the United States. The Senate had voted for the amendment. How would the House of Representatives vote?

Capitol Hill churned with people, waiting to get into the House.

"Congress'll vote for the amendment same as the Senate," said Mrs. Green confidently.

Mr. Green remained silent awhile, tugging at his beard. "I'm not so sure Congress'll vote for the amendment. I heard most of the Democrats are against it."

"It can't be so, I hope it isn't," cried Mrs. Green. Her voice trembled a little. This was something she was paying for. Her son, Henry, was in the hospital with an ugly wound in his side. "If the Constitution isn't amended there'll be no law against slavery; all the bloodshed will be for nothing."

"I'd like to hear the debate," said Mr. Green, trying to inch a little nearer to the great bronze doors. "Never saw such a crowd."

"I hope we can get in and hear what they say, so we can tell Henry just what happened," said Mrs. Green.

A group of crinolined women had managed to wedge in.

"If we don't get in, Nancy'll tell Henry what happened. I think I see her there with those women. She told me she'd get in somehow," smiled Mr. Green.

The crinolined ladies had a determined air; nothing could stop them. They stormed their way into the press gallery, and got in past the gaping crowds. The reporters gave up their seats.

The House was crowded from wall to wall, every inch of standing room was taken. Senators had come in a body to stand on the floor to watch and listen. The Secretary of State had come in, and the Postmaster General. The four Justices, and Chief Justice Chase appeared presently. Visitors craned their necks to see the galaxy of notables. Those who had not been able to get into the House, stood in the corridors and lobbies, tier upon tier of faces, one behind the other; everyone straining to see and to hear what was going on.

A low hum of excitement buzzed in the air like a prelude to an opera. "When will it begin?" asked Mrs. Green in a loud whisper. She could hardly see anything from her place in the corridor.

"Shh," warned several voices.

"These are only the preliminaries of the meeting going on now," explained a tall man in front of Mrs. Green.

"What's going to happen now?" a woman asked.

"The resolution to amend the Constitution's come up for a final decision," explained the tall man in an important voice.

"Shh," hissed several voices.

The guard at the door made desperate gestures for silence.

The debate had started: long heckling speeches and sharp pithy remarks followed each other in rapid succession.

"We'll know pretty soon how the wind blows," said Mr. Green.

"They're talking too much, it's taking too long. When will the voting begin?" Mrs. Green asked wearily as time dragged on.

"The Speaker has ordered the final roll call," announced the tall man. The crowd in the corridors and lobbies pressed forward.

A loud clapping of hands, and of cheers, broke out every time a Congressman, who had been expected to vote Nay, voted Aye. The Speaker pounded his gavel when the applause was prolonged.

"A two-third vote is needed to carry the resolution," said the tall man.

Pencils were taken out, jotting down the Ayes and Nays. Suddenly the Speaker of the House asked that his name be called.

"That's unusual," said the tall man. "The vote must be pretty close."

"Aye," shouted the Speaker when his name was called.

Long hand clapping and loud cheers broke out. The Speaker pounded his gavel, but cheers and hand clapping grew louder.

The Clerk leaned over and whispered to the Speaker.

"One hundred and nineteen Ayes and fifty-six Nays," announced the Speaker in a loud ringing voice.

A strange quietness followed, as if each one held his breath. Then suddenly a great shout broke into cheers and cries of joy. Men clapped their hands and shouted, "The Thirteenth Amendment to the Constitution is passed."

"Slavery is abolished from the United States."

The victory came by a margin of only three votes; men told each other that, in wonder, shaking hands. Others jumped up on their seats and shouted, "God bless Abraham Lincoln, God bless the Thirty-Seventh Congress!" Women were waving handkerchiefs, some were weeping for joy.

"I move we adjourn in honor of this immortal and sublime event," proposed a representative from Illinois.

Salutes from a hundred guns thundered from Capitol Hill. The streets were a pandemonium of shouting, dancing, songs of joy.

Mrs. Green wept softly as she made her sedate way through the crowds. Slavery was to be no more—"God bless Abraham Lincoln, God bless the Congress," she whispered.

Henry lay very still, listening to Mrs. Green and Nancy tell him what happened at the House of Representatives. When he moved ever so slightly, he felt the sharp pain in his side. But he forgot the pain in the excitement of the moment. "The war will soon be over," he exclaimed, with a quick gesture that made him wince. "Yes, it will soon be over. Sherman has taken Atlanta and Grant is annihilating Lee's army. The rebels will sue for peace."

"God grant it may be soon," exclaimed Mrs. Green.

"It will," Henry assured her. "We will be a united nation now, no longer half free, half slave. I am glad I helped a little."

A large crowd, and a brass band came to the White House, shouting for the president. They were celebrating the Thirteenth Amendment, serenading the man behind it. Lincoln came to the window to look down into the sea of faces with a radiant smile, but there was a solemn look in his eyes. There was still much to do; three-fourths of the states must ratify this amendment before it could be written into the Constitution. But he had word that already some states were at work. They would not do it all at once, he knew, but they would do it. He stood there thinking, listening to the voice of the people singing his praise. This was not only his victory. It was a moral victory for the United States, a moral victory for all the world. He said it aloud, talking to the people.

There was a torchlight parade and more singing. So many things might have prevented it—the abolition proclamation might have been questioned, or pronounced illegal—now it was an accomplished fact. He wanted the people to know it—"This amendment," he said, "is a king's cure-all for all evils. It winds the whole thing up—But there is a task yet before us: to go forward . . . ."